POEMS OF
W. S. GILBERT

POEMS OF W. S. GILBERT

Selected by William Cole

ILLUSTRATIONS
BY W. S. GILBERT "BAB"

Thomas Y. Crowell Company, New York

Designed by Sallie Baldwin
Manufactured in the United States of America
L.C. Card 67-15397
1 2 3 4 5 6 7 8 9 10

THE CROWELL POETS

Under the editorship of Lillian Morrison

POEMS OF WILLIAM BLAKE
Selected by Amelia H. Munson

POEMS OF ROBERT BROWNING
Selected by Rosemary Sprague

POEMS OF STEPHEN CRANE
Selected by
Gerald D. McDonald

POEMS OF EMILY DICKINSON
Selected by Helen Plotz

POEMS OF
RALPH WALDO EMERSON
Selected by J. Donald Adams

POEMS OF W. S. GILBERT
Selected by William Cole

POEMS OF ROBERT HERRICK
Selected by
Winfield Townley Scott

POEMS OF JOHN KEATS
Selected by Stanley Kunitz

POEMS OF
HENRY WADSWORTH
LONGFELLOW
Selected by Edmund Fuller

POEMS OF EDGAR ALLAN POE
Selected by Dwight Macdonald

POEMS OF
WILLIAM SHAKESPEARE
Selected by Lloyd Frankenberg

POEMS OF
ALFRED, LORD TENNYSON
Selected by
Ruth Greiner Rausen

POEMS OF WALT WHITMAN
Selected by
Lawrence Clark Powell

POEMS OF
WILLIAM WORDSWORTH
Selected by Elinor Parker

CONTENTS

I. "HE LED HIS REGIMENT FROM BEHIND": *Of Military Matters* 11

II. "A MAN WHO WOULD WOO A FAIR MAID": *Love Pro and Con* 27

III. "SPURN NOT THE NOBLY BORN": *Kings, Queens, and Other High Rankers* 51

IV. "LIST WHILE THE POET TROLLS": *Some Ridiculous Stories* 69

V. "NEVER, NEVER SICK AT SEA": *Admirals, Captains, and Jolly Jack Tars* 101

VI. "ROLL ON, THOU BALL, ROLL ON!": *The Way of the World* 115

VII. "THE MEANING DOESN'T MATTER": *A Miscellany of Characters* 129

Notes 149

Index of Titles 159

Index of First Lines 161

POEMS OF W. S. GILBERT

W. S. GILBERT

"I have been scribbling twaddle for thirty-five years to suit the public taste," wrote W.S. Gilbert at the close of a career that embraced some ninety plays, a dozen operettas that have become unparalleled classics, and the funniest humorous poetry in the English language.

The art of humor is seldom taken seriously enough, and Gilbert's attitude toward his own art was no exception; he was a magnificent craftsman, and he knew it. He could build a complicated plot, with logic and suspense; he could handle the most intricate rhyme-schemes, and could write lyrics that exactly suited any situation. And he never undervalued the commercial worth of his enterprises; in fact, nobody was quicker on the draw with a law suit than he, if he felt he was being exploited. But with all this, and with his great success, he carried a grudge against the public —they hadn't fully appreciated his "serious" plays, written and produced early in his career. The public, apparently, was right; from all accounts the serious plays were terrible. The situation was positively Gilbertian (a word which the dictionary defines as meaning anything humorously topsy-turvy): to belittle his true art and build up his unimportant work.

William Schwenck Gilbert was born of well-to-do parents in London in 1836. The first dramatic incident of his life came at the age of two, when he was traveling with his parents in Italy; it sounds as unlikely as something from one of his own operettas, but he was kidnapped by Italian brigands and had to be ransomed by his father for one hundred and twenty five pounds. In his early years he was educated in France and England, and then graduated from King's College at the University of London. He apparently dabbled in light verse in his teens, and one example still exists. It seems that he had had his head shaven as a result of typhoid fever. In this shorn state, in Paris, he happened to witness a procession which included Napoleon III and the Empress Eugenie. His reaction has been preserved:

To the Emperor she said:
"How beautiful the head
Of that youth of gallant mein,
Cropped so neat and close and clean—
Though I owe he's rather lean."
Said the Emperor: "It is!
And I never saw a phiz
More wonderful than 'is."

After college, Gilbert worked for four tiresome years as an office clerk, studying law in the evenings. He married and became a barrister-at-law in 1866, and was a practising but unenthusiastic lawyer for the next four years. During all this time he had been contributing light verse illustrated by himself to the magazine *Fun*, an inferior imitation of *Punch*. He signed the illustrations "Bab"—a childhood nickname, the shortening of "Baby"—and the poems became known as *The Bab Ballads*. His biographer writes that originally Gilbert submitted an early Bab ballad—"The Yarn of the Nancy Bell"—to *Punch* and that it was turned down because it was considered too cannibalistic. Gilbert himself scoffed at the verses, claiming that since he had to turn out one a week for *Fun*, they suffered from being written too hastily. When *The Bab Ballads* was published in book form in 1869, he remarked that he had "ventured to publish the little pictures with them, because while they are certainly quite as bad as the ballads, I suppose they are not much worse." This is of course a ridiculous estimate; the drawings are graceful and witty, and superior to the work of most professional cartoonists or illustrators.

Many of the devices—and characters—in *The Bab Ballads*, Gilbert used again, years later, in the Gilbert and Sullivan operettas. For example, "The Bumboat Woman's Story" has both "Little Buttercup" and the terrible curse, "the big, big D," which also appear in *H. M. S. Pinafore*. Gilbert understood the value of a good character or plot twist, and got the maximum mileage from each idea. In the ballads, he is chiefly a satirist, administering sharp kicks to England's overestablished institutions—the church, the state, the military. Hypocrites abound; as the critic Edmund Wilson put it, ". . . characters full of tender and noble sentiments, were shown never to act from any other motives than those of the grimmest self-interest." But there is more than satire in the ballads; there are occasional bursts of pure, wild nonsense, such as when the "Modest Couple" become engaged, "And Peter blushed so hard you might/have heard him miles away." And there are some very funny portraits; there's Private James—"No characteristic trait had he/Of any distinctive kind"—and in the exuberant "Sir Barnaby Bampton Boo," there are the "Women of Tuptonvee/Here is a health to ye/For a Baronet, dears, you would cut off your ears,/Women of Tuptonvee!"

There are about a hundred Bab ballads, and despite their author's estimate, they remain the funniest and most adroit light verse of all time. Some of their humor might be called "black"—such situations as people eating one another, babies being exchanged in their cribs, girls dressed up as sailors, and such characters as gentle Alice Brown, who ". . . assisted dear papa in cutting up a little lad." But they really are so ridiculously exaggerated that they transcend blackness. They are full of elaborate rhymes and intricate, varied meter. Of particular interest is "Lost Mr. Blake" with its long, run-on lines: exactly the style favored today, and almost patented, by Ogden Nash. What I like best about the ballads is their zest, their joyful playfulness; these qualities may be there because the poems were written quickly, but they also show that Gilbert took great pleasure in writing them.

When Gilbert met Arthur Sullivan in 1870, each was already established in his field, Gilbert as a playwright and light-verse poet, and Sullivan as a highly respected composer of serious music. The following year brought forth their first collaboration, *Thespis; or The Gods Grown Old*. It was not a success, but it contained intimations of things to come. Following it, both artists went their separate ways until 1875, when Richard D'Oyly Carte, an enterprising theater manager, brought them together again and commissioned *Trial by Jury*, which was performed as an afterpiece to Offenbach's *La Périchole*. It was a great success; the idea of an Englishman lampooning an English institution—in this case, the law—and doing it with such verve caught the public's sense of humor, and *Trial by Jury* ran for nine months. At D'Oyly Carte's instigation—he had by then founded a theater devoted to light opera by contemporary Englishmen—the pair collaborated on *The Sorcerer*, which had a modest success, and then produced, in 1878, *H. M. S. Pinafore*, which rocketed them to the heights of fame.

Although Gilbert and Sullivan are associated in the public mind as closely as Hansel and Gretel and Damon and Pythias, they were really an odd combination, and not particularly good friends. Gilbert was hot-tempered, witty, and suspicious of other people's motives; Sullivan was mild, gregarious, and active in his social life. Through all the years of their collaboration, they never addressed one another by their first names; the correspondence was always "Dear Gilbert" and "Dear Sullivan." The closest they got to intimacy was "Dear G." and "Dear S." When the score of an operetta was finished, Sullivan would go on to other pursuits, but Gilbert would dig in and direct the production. He was a perfectionist. He would select the actors, supervise the costuming, and work out the action on a model stage, using little blocks of wood for furniture and actors. As a matter of fact, he regarded most live actors as blocks of wood, and could be a tyrannical taskmaster, although scrupulously fair-minded if an actor tried to give him what he wanted.

Gilbert and Sullivan collaborated in person surprisingly seldom. Gilbert, struck with an idea, would communicate just the bare outline of a plot to Sullivan. If Sullivan liked it, Gilbert would painstakingly work out a story line, go through many drafts, and bring the almost completed libretto to the composer. Sullivan would then write the score, and completely orchestrate it (without the use of a piano, oddly enough). There would, of course, be some back-and-forth, adjusting lyrics to music and vice versa, but generally each man stuck to his own field. Gilbert, in fact, always claimed to be totally unmusical; he is credited with the famous saying, "I know two tunes. One is 'God Save the Queen,' and the other isn't." As the Gilbert and Sullivan collaboration continued, and their fame and fortune increased, each became more and more discontented with his dependence on the other. Each had worked with other collaborators with indifferent results; it appeared that only with one another could they strike that really magical spark. More and more Sullivan complained about the lightness of the operettas. He wanted something meatier, something approaching grand opera, and after their twelfth collaboration, *The Gondoliers*, he set off Gilbert's hot temper by intimating that he had been forced to work with trivial material. Gilbert wrote him: "Are you under the impression that you have been effacing yourself in all our pieces? If you mean that I am to supply a libretto subordinate to the music, consequently making the librettist subordinate to the composer, then there is no way to be found that would be satisfactory to both. You are as adept at your profession as I am at mine. If we meet it must be Master and Master, not as Master and Servant."

As it turned out, they did not meet again or work as collaborators for a period of four years, during which time Sullivan composed serious music and Gilbert collaborated, unsuccessfully, with two other composers. When they were finally brought together again, they wrote two further operettas, *Utopia, Limited*, in 1893, and *The Grand Duke*, in 1896, but the zing was gone; the operettas, although respectable and full of nuggets, have never been as popular as the earlier delightful dozen.

The first fascination with Gilbert and Sullivan operettas usually comes in the early teens, and it can develop into a life-long mania. "Savoyards"—so named after D'Oyly Carte's Savoy Theatre, where most of the Gilbert and Sullivan productions were performed—can remember the lyrics of most of the songs, can find an apt quotation from somewhere in some operetta to fit almost any situation, and can spend hours comparing the relative merits of every Ko-Ko and Yum-Yum they've seen. My own family, alas, were not Savoyards. I can remember an incident from the height of my own mania, when I was fifteen. I was seated at dinner with a dozen talkative adult relatives. Dinnertime unfortunately coincided with the weekly Gilbert and Sullivan hour on the radio, which I *couldn't* miss. Surreptitiously I had placed the table radio on the sideboard behind my chair, and had *The Mikado* turned on, very soft. But not soft enough, for one of my numerous aunts said, "Billy—turn the radio off—we can't hear ourselves *think!*" Since it was the kind of household where the children did *not* run things, I complied. It was enough to put a kid off adults for life.

Gilbert can be a marvelous teacher for a fifteen-year-old

boy. He says "things are seldom what they seem." He recommends that the pompous always be kidded, and shows that no man-made institutions are sacred. He exposes hypocrisy and instills a healthy skepticism. But most of all, he introduces the delights of language, demonstrates the flexibility of the English tongue. He does wonders for a limited vocabulary. Where else would a boy pick up—and be able to drop casually in a conversation—such beauties as "residuum," "vagaries," "peripatetic," or "panoply." And consider the delight of the overblown language used by the irate Sir Joseph Porter when a sailor dared to curse "damme!" in front of the ladies:

Go, ribald, get you hence
To your cabin with celerity.
This is the consequence
Of ill-advised asperity!

* * * *

In the late 1890s, Gilbert cut down on his activities and spent most of his time at his handsome country house, Grim's Dyke, where he lived the good life with twenty servants in attendance. He worked on an operetta with the composer Edward German, which was produced unsuccessfully in 1909, but most of his time was devoted to keeping track of Gilbert and Sullivan productions all over the world, sitting as a justice of the peace, and writing irate letters-to-the-editor. (Incidentally, his letter-writing style was a delight, as witness his reply to a stranger's query about an impending world's fair: "Sir, I view the proposal to hold an international exhibit at San Francisco with an equanimity bordering on indifference.") He had a grumpy but happy old age. At a dinner held in his honor, he brought down the house by opening his address with a quote from *Princess Ida*: "Yet everybody says I'm such a disagreeable man! /And I can't think why!"

In 1911, at the age of seventy-four, he died of a heart attack while rescuing a young woman from drowning in his own swimming pool. A few years earlier he had written that the ideal place to die would be in his own garden on a sunny afternoon. And that is pretty much the way it happened.

I.

"HE LED HIS REGIMENT FROM BEHIND"

Of Military Matters

THE DUKE OF PLAZA-TORO

From *The Gondoliers*

In enterprise of martial kind,
When there was any fighting,
He led his regiment from behind
(He found it less exciting).
But when away his regiment ran,
His place was at the fore, O—
That celebrated,
Cultivated,
Underrated
Nobleman,
The Duke of Plaza-Toro!
In the first and foremost flight, ha, ha!
You always found that knight, ha, ha!
That celebrated,
Cultivated,
Underrated
Nobleman,
The Duke of Plaza-Toro!

When, to evade Destruction's hand,
To hide they all proceeded,
No soldier in that gallant band
Hid half as well as he did.
He lay concealed throughout the war,
And so preserved his gore, O!
That unaffected,
Undetected,
Well connected
Warrior,
The Duke of Plaza-Toro!
In every doughty deed, ha, ha!
He always took the lead, ha, ha!
That unaffected,
Undetected,
Well connected
Warrior,
The Duke of Plaza-Toro!

When told that they would all be shot
Unless they left the service,
That hero hesitated not,
So marvellous his nerve is.
He sent his resignation in,
The first of all his corps, O!
That very knowing,
Overflowing,
Easy-going
Paladin,
The Duke of Plaza-Toro!

To men of grosser clay, ha, ha!
He always showed the way, ha, ha!
That very knowing,
Overflowing,
Easy-going
Paladin,
The Duke of Plaza-Toro!

GENERAL JOHN

The bravest names for fire and flames
And all that mortal durst,
Were General John and Private James,
Of the Sixty-seventy-first.

General John was a soldier tried,
A chief of warlike dons;
A haughty stride and a withering pride
Were Major-General John's.

A sneer would play on his martial phiz,
Superior birth to show;
"Pish!" was a favourite word of his,
And he often said "Ho! ho!"

FULL-PRIVATE JAMES described might be,
As a man of a mournful mind;
No characteristic trait had he
Of any distinctive kind.

From the ranks, one day, cried PRIVATE JAMES,
"Oh! MAJOR-GENERAL JOHN,
I've doubts of our respective names,
My mournful mind upon.

"A glimmering thought occurs to me
(Its source I can't unearth),
But I've a kind of a notion we
Were cruelly changed at birth.

"I've a strange idea that each other's names
We've each of us here got on.
Such things have been," said PRIVATE JAMES.
"They have!" sneered GENERAL JOHN.

"My GENERAL JOHN, I swear upon
My oath I think 'tis so——"
"Pish" proudly sneered his GENERAL JOHN,
And he also said "Ho! ho!"

"My GENERAL JOHN! my GENERAL JOHN!
My GENERAL JOHN!" quoth he,
"This aristocratical sneer upon
Your face I blush to see!

"No truly great or generous cove
Deserving of them names,
Would sneer at a fixed idea that's drove
In the mind of a PRIVATE JAMES!"

Said GENERAL JOHN, "Upon your claims
No need your breath to waste;
If this is a joke, FULL-PRIVATE JAMES,
It's a joke of doubtful taste.

"But, being a man of doubtless worth,
  If you feel certain quite
That we were probably changed at birth,
  I'll venture to say you're right."

So General John as Private James
  Fell in, parade upon;
And Private James, by change of names,
  Was Major-General John.

THE HEAVY DRAGOON

From *Patience*

If you want a receipt for that popular mystery,
  Known to the world as a Heavy Dragoon,
Take all the remarkable people in history,
  Rattle them off to a popular tune!
The pluck of LORD NELSON on board of the *Victory*—
  Genius of BISMARCK devising a plan;
The humour of FIELDING (which sounds contradictory)—
  Coolness of PAGET about to trepan—
The grace of MOZART, that unparalleled musico—
  Wit of MACAULAY, who wrote of QUEEN ANNE—
The pathos of PADDY, as rendered by BOUCICAULT—
  Style of the BISHOP OF SODOR AND MAN—
The dash of a D'ORSAY, divested of quackery—
Narrative powers of DICKENS and THACKERAY—
VICTOR EMMANUEL—peak-haunting PEVERIL—
THOMAS AQUINAS, and DOCTOR SACHEVERELL—
  TUPPER and TENNYSON—DANIEL DEFOE—
  ANTHONY TROLLOPE and MISTER GUIZOT!

Take of these elements all that is fusible,
Melt 'em all down in a pipkin or crucible,
Set 'em to simmer and take off the scum,
And a Heavy Dragoon is the residuum!

If you want a receipt for this soldierlike paragon,
Get at the wealth of the CZAR (if you can)—
The family pride of a Spaniard from Aragon—
Force of MEPHISTO pronouncing a ban—
A smack of LORD WATERFORD, reckless and rollicky—
Swagger of RODERICK, heading his clan—
The keen penetration of PADDINGTON POLLACKY—
Grace of an Odalisque on a divan—
The genius strategic of CAESAR or HANNIBAL—
Skill of LORD WOLSELEY in thrashing a cannibal—
Flavour of HAMLET—the STRANGER, a touch of him—
Little of MANFRED (but not very much of him)—
Beadle of Burlington—RICHARDSON's show—
MR. MICAWBER and MADAME TUSSAUD!
Take of these elements all that is fusible—
Melt 'em all down in a pipkin or crucible—
Set 'em to simmer and take off the scum,
And a Heavy Dragoon is the residuum!

THE CONTEMPLATIVE SENTRY

From *Iolanthe*

When all night long a chap remains
   On sentry-go, to chase monotony
He exercises of his brains,
   That is, assuming that he's got any.
Though never nurtured in the lap
   Of luxury, yet I admonish you,
I am an intellectual chap,
   And think of things that would astonish you.
      I often think it's comical
         How Nature always does contrive
      That every boy and every gal,
         That's born into the world alive,
      Is either a little Liberal,
         Or else a little Conservative!
            Fal lal la!

When in that house M. P.'s divide,
If they've a brain and cerebellum, too,
They've got to leave that brain outside,
And vote just as their leaders tell 'em to.
But then the prospect of a lot
Of statesmen, all in close proximity,
A-thinking for themselves, is what
No man can face with equanimity.
Then let's rejoice with loud Fal lal
That Nature wisely does contrive
That every boy and every gal,
That's born into the world alive,
Is either a little Liberal,
Or else a little Conservative!
Fal lal la!

ARAC'S SONG

From *Princess Ida*

This helmet, I suppose,
Was meant to ward off blows,
It's very hot,
And weighs a lot,
As many a guardsman knows,
So off that helmet goes.

This tight-fitting cuirass
Is but a useless mass,
        It's made of steel,
        And weighs a deal,
A man is but an ass
Who fights in a cuirass,
So off goes that cuirass.

These brassets, truth to tell,
May look uncommon well,
        But in a fight,
        They're much too tight,
They're like a lobster shell!

These things I treat the same
(I quite forget their name),
        They turn one's legs
        To cribbage pegs—
Their aid I thus disclaim,
Though I forget their name!

THE MODERN MAJOR-GENERAL

From *The Pirates of Penzance*

I am the very pattern of a modern Major-Gineral,
I've information vegetable, animal, and mineral;
I know the kings of England, and I quote the fights
historical,
From Marathon to Waterloo, in order categorical;
I'm very well acquainted, too, with matters mathematical,
I understand equations, both the simple and quadratical;
About binomial theorem I'm teeming with a lot o' news,
With interesting facts about the square of the hypotenuse.
I'm very good at integral and differential calculus,
I know the scientific names of beings animalculous.
In short, in matters vegetable, animal, and mineral,
I am the very model of a modern Major-Gineral.

I know our mythic history—KING ARTHUR's and SIR
CARADOC's,
I answer hard acrostics, I've a pretty taste for paradox;

I quote in elegiacs all the crimes of HELIOGABALUS,
In conics I can floor peculiarities parabolous.
I tell undoubted RAPHAELS from GERARD Dows and
ZOFFANIES,
I know the croaking chorus from the "Frogs" of
ARISTOPHANES;
Then I can hum a fugue, of which I've heard the music's
din afore,
And whistle all the airs from that confounded nonsense
"Pinafore."
Then I can write a washing-bill in Babylonic cuneiform,
And tell you every detail of CARACTACUS's uniform.
In short, in matters vegetable, animal, and mineral,
I am the very model of a modern Major-Gineral.

In fact, when I know what is meant by "mamelon" and
"ravelin,"
When I can tell at sight a Chassepôt rifle from a javelin,
When such affairs as *sorties* and surprises I'm more wary at,
And when I know precisely what is meant by Commissariat,
When I have learnt what progress has been made in
modern gunnery,
When I know more of tactics than a novice in a nunnery,
In short, when I've a smattering of elementary strategy,
You'll say a better Major-Gener*al* has never *sat* a gee—
For my military knowledge, though I'm plucky and
adventury,
Has only been brought down to the beginning of the
century.
But still in learning vegetable, animal, and mineral,
I am the very model of a modern Major-Gineral!

II.

"A MAN WHO WOULD WOO A FAIR MAID"

Love Pro and Con

A MAN WHO WOULD WOO A FAIR MAID

From *The Yeomen of the Guard*

A man who would woo a fair maid,
Should 'prentice himself to the trade;
    And study all day,
    In methodical way,
How to flatter, cajole, and persuade.
He should 'prentice himself at fourteen,
And practise from morning to e'en;
    And when he's of age,
    If he will, I'll engage,
He may capture the heart of a queen!
        It is purely a matter of skill,
        Which all may attain if they will:
            But every Jack
            He must study the knack
        If he wants to make sure of his Jill!

If he's made the best use of his time,
His twig he'll so carefully lime
That every bird
Will come down at his word,
Whatever its plumage and clime.
He must learn that the thrill of a touch
May mean little, or nothing, or much;
It's an instrument rare,
To be handled with care,
And ought to be treated as such.
It is purely a matter of skill,
Which all may attain if they will:
But every Jack,
He must study the knack
If he wants to make sure of his Jill!

Then a glance may be timid or free;
It will vary in mighty degree,
From an impudent stare
To a look of despair
That no maid without pity can see.
And a glance of despair is no guide—
It may have its ridiculous side;
It may draw you a tear
Or a box on the ear;
You can never be sure till you've tried.
It is purely a matter of skill,
Which all may attain if they will:
But every Jack
He must study the knack
If he wants to make sure of his Jill!

THE SUICIDE'S GRAVE

From *The Mikado*

On a tree by a river a little tomtit
Sang "Willow, titwillow, titwillow!"
And I said to him, "Dicky-bird, why do you sit
Singing 'Willow, titwillow, titwillow'?
Is it weakness of intellect, birdie?" I cried,
"Or a rather tough worm in your little inside?"
With a shake of his poor little head he replied,
"Oh, willow, titwillow, titwillow!"

He slapped at his chest, as he sat on that bough,
Singing, "Willow, titwillow, titwillow!"
And a cold perspiration bespangled his brow,

Oh, willow, titwillow, titwillow!
He sobbed and he sighed, and a gurgle he gave,
Then he threw himself into thc billowy wave,
And an echo arose from the suicide's grave—
"Oh, willow, titwillow, titwillow!"

Now I feel just as sure as I'm sure that my name
Isn't Willow, titwillow, titwillow,
That 'twas blighted affection that made him exclaim,
"Oh, willow, titwillow, titwillow!"
And if you remain callous and obdurate, I
Shall perish as he did, and you will know why,
Though I probably shall not exclaim as I die,
"Oh, willow, titwillow, titwillow!"

GENTLE ALICE BROWN

It was a robber's daughter, and her name was Alice Brown,
Her father was the terror of a small Italian town;
Her mother was a foolish, weak, but amiable old thing;
But it isn't of her parents that I'm going for to sing.

As Alice was a-sitting at her window-sill one day
A beautiful young gentleman he chanced to pass that way;
She cast her eyes upon him, and he looked so good and true,
That she thought, "I could be happy with a gentleman
like you!"

And every morning passed her house that cream of
gentlemen,
She knew she might expect him at a quarter unto ten,
A sorter in the Custom-house, it was his daily road
(The Custom-house was fifteen minutes' walk from her
abode).

But ALICE was a pious girl, who knew it wasn't wise
To look at strange young sorters with expressive purple
eyes;
So she sought the village priest to whom her family
confessed—
The priest by whom their little sins were carefully assessed.

"Oh, holy father," ALICE said, " 'twould grieve you, would
it not?
To discover that I was a most disreputable lot!
Of all unhappy sinners I'm the most unhappy one."
The padre said, "Whatever have you been and gone and
done?"

"I have helped mamma to steal a little kiddy from its dad,
I've assisted dear papa in cutting up a little lad.
I've planned a little burglary and forged a little cheque,
And slain a little baby for the coral on its neck!"

The worthy pastor heaved a sigh, and dropped a silent
tear—
And said, "You mustn't judge yourself too heavily, my
dear—

It's wrong to murder babies, little corals for to fleece;
But sins like these one expiates at half-a-crown apiece.

"Girls will be girls—you're very young, and flighty in
your mind;
Old heads upon young shoulders we must not expect to
find:
We mustn't be too hard upon these little girlish tricks—
Let's see—five crimes at half-a-crown—exactly twelve-
and-six."

"Oh, father," little ALICE cried, "your kindness makes me
weep,
You do these little things for me so singularly cheap—
Your thoughtful liberality I never can forget;
But oh, there is another crime I haven't mentioned yet!

"A pleasant-looking gentleman, with pretty purple eyes—
I've noticed at my window, as I've sat a-catching flies;
He passes by it every day as certain as can be—
I blush to say I've winked at him, and he has winked at me!"

"For shame," said FATHER PAUL, "my erring daughter! On my word
This is the most distressing news that I have ever heard.
Why, naughty girl, your excellent papa has pledged your hand
To a promising young robber, the lieutenant of his band!

"This dreadful piece of news will pain your worthy parents so!
They are the most remunerative customers I know;
For many many years they've kept starvation from my doors,
I never knew so criminal a family as yours!

"The common country folk in this insipid neighbourhood
Have nothing to confess, they're so ridiculously good;
And if you marry any one respectable at all,
Why, you'll reform, and what will then become of FATHER PAUL?"

The worthy priest, he up and drew his cowl upon his crown,
And started off in haste to tell the news to ROBBER BROWN;
To tell him how his daughter, who was now for marriage fit,
Had winked upon a sorter, who reciprocated it.

Good ROBBER BROWN he muffled up his anger pretty well,
He said, "I have a notion, and that notion I will tell;
I will nab this gay young sorter, terrify him into fits,
And get my gentle wife to chop him into little bits.

"I've studied human nature, and I know a thing or two;
Though a girl may fondly love a living gent, as many do,
A feeling of disgust upon her senses there will fall
When she looks upon his body chopped particularly small."

He traced that gallant sorter to a still suburban square;
He watched his opportunity and seized him unaware;
He took a life-preserver and he hit him on the head,
And MRS. BROWN dissected him before she went to bed.

And pretty little ALICE grew more settled in her mind,
She never more was guilty of a weakness of the kind,
Until at length good ROBBER BROWN bestowed her pretty hand
On the promising young robber, the lieutenant of his band.

THE MAGNET AND THE CHURN

From *Patience*

A magnet hung in a hardware shop,
And all around was a loving crop
Of scissors and needles, nails and knives,
Offering love for all their lives;
But for iron the Magnet felt no whim,
Though he charmed iron, it charmed not him,
From needles and nails and knives he'd turn,
For he'd set his love on a Silver Churn!
His most aesthetic,
Very magnetic
Fancy took this turn—
"If I can wheedle
A knife or needle,
Why not a Silver Churn?"

And Iron and Steel expressed surprise,
The needles opened their well-drilled eyes,
The pen-knives felt "shut up," no doubt,
The scissors declared themselves "cut out,"
The kettles they boiled with rage, 'tis said,
While every nail went off its head,
And hither and thither began to roam,
Till a hammer came up—and drove it home,

While this magnetic
Peripatetic
Lover he lived to learn,
By no endeavor,
Can Magnet ever
Attract a Silver Churn!

FERDINANDO AND ELVIRA
OR, THE GENTLE PIEMAN

PART I

At a pleasant evening party I had taken down to supper
One whom I will call ELVIRA, and we talked of love and
TUPPER,

MR. TUPPER and the poets, very lightly with them dealing,
For I've always been distinguished for a strong poetic
feeling.

Then we let off paper crackers, each of which contained a
motto,
And she listened while I read them, till her mother told
her not to.

Then she whispered, "To the ball-room we had better,
dear, be walking;

If we stop down here much longer, really people will be
talking."

There were noblemen in coronets, and military cousins,
There were captains by the hundred, there were baronets
by dozens.

Yet she heeded not their offers, but dismissed them with
a blessing;
Then she let down all her back hair which had taken long
in dressing.

Then she had convulsive sobbings in her agitated throttle,
Then she wiped her pretty eyes and smelt her pretty
smelling-bottle.

So I whispered, "DEAR ELVIRA, say—what can the matter
be with you?
Does anything you've eaten, darling POPSY, disagree with
you?"

But in spite of all I said, her sob grew more and more
distressing.
And she tore her pretty back hair, which had taken long
in dressing.

Then she gazed upon the carpet, at the ceiling then above
me,
And she whispered, "FERDINANDO, do you really, *really*
love me?"

"Love you?" said I, then I sighed, and then I gazed
upon her sweetly—
For I think I do this sort of thing particularly neatly —

"Send me to the Arctic regions, or illimitable azure,
On a scientific goose-chase, with my COXWELL or my
GLAISHER.

"Tell me whither I may hie me, tell me, dear one, that I
may know—
Is it up the highest Andes? down a horrible volcano?"

But she said, "It isn't polar bears, or hot volcanic grottoes,
Only find out who it is that writes those lovely cracker
mottoes!"

PART II

"Tell me, HENRY WADSWORTH, ALFRED, POET CLOSE, or
MISTER TUPPER,
Do you write the bonbon mottoes my ELVIRA pulls at
supper?"

But HENRY WADSWORTH smiled, and said he had not had
that honour;
And ALFRED, too, disclaimed the words that told so much
upon her.

"MISTER MARTIN TUPPER, POET CLOSE, I beg of you
inform us";
But my question seemed to throw them both into a rage
enormous.

Mister Close expressed a wish that he could only get
anigh to me.
And Mister Martin Tupper sent the following reply to
me:—
"A fool is bent upon a twig, but wise men dread a bandit."
Which I think must have been clever, for I didn't
understand it.

Seven weary years I wandered—Patagonia, China,
Norway,
Till at last I sank exhausted at a pastrycook his doorway.

There were fuchsias and geraniums, and daffodils and
myrtle,
So I entered, and I ordered half a basin of mock turtle.

He was plump and he was chubby, he was smooth and he
was rosy,
And his little wife was pretty, and particularly cosy.

And he chirped and sang, and skipped about, and laughed
with laughter hearty—
He was wonderfully active for so very stout a party.

And I said, "Oh, gentle pieman, why so very, very merry?
Is it purity of conscience, or your one-and-seven sherry?"

But he answered, "I'm so happy—no profession could be
dearer—
If I am not humming 'Tra! la! la!' I'm singing, 'Tirer,
lirer!'

"First I go and make the patties, and the puddings and
the jellies,
Then I make a sugar birdcage, which upon a table swell is;

"Then I polish all the silver, which a supper-table
lacquers;
Then I write the pretty mottoes which you find inside the
crackers"—

"Found at last!" I madly shouted. "Gentle pieman,
you astound me!"
Then I waved the turtle soup enthusiastically round me.

And I shouted and I danced until he'd quite a crowd
around him—
And I rushed away, exclaiming, "I have found him! I
have found him!"

And I heard the gentle pieman in the road behind me
trilling,
"'Tira! lira!' stop him, stop him! 'Tra! la! la! la!' the
soup's a shilling!"

But until I reached ELVIRA's home, I never, never waited,
And ELVIRA to her FERDINAND's irrevocably mated!

TO PHOEBE

"Gentle, modest, little flower,
  Sweet epitome of May,
Love me but for half-an-hour,
  Love me, love me, little fay."
Sentences so fiercely flaming
  In your tiny shell-like ear,
I should always be exclaiming
  If I loved you, PHOEBE, dear.

"Smiles that thrill from any distance
  Shed upon me while I sing!
Please ecstaticise existence,
  Love me, oh thou fairy thing!"
Words like these, outpouring sadly,
  You'd perpetually hear,
If I loved you, fondly, madly;—
  But I do not, PHOEBE, dear.

THE MODEST COUPLE

When man and maiden meet, I like to see a drooping eye,
I always droop my own—I am the shyest of the shy.
I'm also fond of bashfulness, and sitting down on thorns,
For modesty's a quality that womankind adorns.

Whenever I am introduced to any pretty maid,
My knees they knock together, just as if I were afraid;
I flutter, and I stammer, and I turn a pleasing red,
For to laugh, and flirt, and ogle I consider most ill-bred.

But still in all these matters, as in other things below,
There is a proper medium, as I'm about to show.
I do not recommend a newly-married pair to try
To carry on as PETER carried on with SARAH BLIGH.

Betrothed they were when very young—before they'd
learnt to speak
(For Sarah was but six days old, and Peter was a week);
Though little more than babies at those early ages, yet
They bashfully would faint when they occasionally met.

They blushed, and flushed, and fainted, till they reached
the age of nine,
When Peter's good papa (he was a Baron of the Rhine)
Determined to endeavour some sound argument to find
To bring these shy young people to a proper frame of mind.

He told them that as Sarah was to be his Peter's bride,
They might at least consent to sit at table side by side;
He begged that they would now and then shake hands, till
he was hoarse,
Which Sarah thought indelicate, and Peter very coarse.

And Peter in a tremble to the blushing maid would say,
"You must excuse papa, Miss Bligh,—it is his mountain
way."
Says Sarah, "His behaviour I'll endeavour to forget,
But your papa's the coarsest person that I ever met.

"He plighted us without our leave, when we were very
young,
Before we had begun articulating with the tongue.
His underbred suggestions fill your Sarah with alarm;
Why, gracious me! he'll ask us next to walk out arm-in-
arm!"

At length when SARAH reached the legal age of twenty-one,
The Baron he determined to unite her to his son;
And SARAH in a fainting-fit for weeks unconscious lay,
And PETER blushed so hard you might have heard him
miles away.

And when the time arrived for taking SARAH to his heart,
They were married in two churches half-a-dozen miles
apart
(Intending to escape all public ridicule and chaff),
And the service was conducted by electric telegraph.

And when it was concluded, and the priest had said his say,
Until the time arrived when they were both to drive away,
They never spoke or offered for to fondle or to fawn,
For *he* waited in the attic, and *she* waited on the lawn.

At length, when four o'clock arrived, and it was time to go,
The carriage was announced, but decent SARAH answered
"No!

Upon my word, I'd rather sleep my everlasting nap,
Than go and ride alone with MR. PETER in a trap."

And PETER's over-sensitive and highly-polished mind
Wouldn't suffer him to sanction a proceeding of the kind;
And further, he declared he suffered overwhelming shocks
At the bare idea of having any coachman on the box.

So PETER into one turn-out incontinently rushed,
While SARAH in a second trap sat modestly and blushed;
And MR. NEWMAN's coachman, on authority I've heard,
Drove away in gallant style upon the coach-box of a third.

Now, though this modest couple in the matter of the car
Were very likely carrying a principle too far,
I hold their shy behaviour was more laudable in them
Than that of PETER's brother with MISS SARAH's sister EM.

ALPHONSO, who in cool assurance all creation licks,
He up and said to EMMIE (who had impudence for six),
"MISS EMILY, I love you—will you marry? Say the
word!"
And EMILY said, "Certainly, ALPHONSO, like a bird!"

I do not recommend a newly-married pair to try
To carry on as PETER carried on with SARAH BLIGH,
But still their shy behaviour was more laudable in them
Than that of PETER's brother with MISS SARAH's sister EM.

III.

"SPURN NOT THE NOBLY BORN"

Kings, Queens, and Other High Rankers

BLUE BLOOD

From *Iolanthe*

Spurn not the nobly born
With love affected,
Nor treat with virtuous scorn
The well connected.
High rank involves no shame—
We boast an equal claim
With him of humble name
To be respected!
Blue blood! Blue blood!
When virtuous love is sought,
Thy power is naught,
Though dating from the Flood,
Blue blood!

Spare us the bitter pain
  Of stern denials,
Nor with low born disdain
  Augment our trials.
Hearts just as pure and fair
May beat in Belgrave Square
As in the lowly air
  Of Seven Dials!
      Blue blood! Blue blood!
        Of what avail art thou
          To serve me now?
      Though dating from the Flood,
          Blue blood!

KING GOODHEART

From *The Gondoliers*

There lived a King, as I've been told
In the wonder-working days of old,
When hearts were twice as good as gold,
 And twenty times as mellow.
Good temper triumphed in his face,
And in his heart he found a place
For all the erring human race
 And every wretched fellow.
When he had Rhenish wine to drink
It made him very sad to think
That some, at junket or at jink,
 Must be content with toddy:
He wished all men as rich as he
(And he was rich as rich could be),
So to the top of every three
 Promoted everybody.

Ambassadors cropped up like hay,
Prime Ministers and such as they
Grew like asparagus in May,

And Dukes were three a penny:
Lord Chancellors were cheap as sprats,
And Bishops in their shovel hats
Were plentiful as tabby cats—
If possible, too many.
On every side Field-Marshals gleamed,
Small beer were Lords-Lieutenants deemed,
With Admirals the ocean teemed,
All round his wide dominions;
And Party Leaders you might meet
In twos and threes in every street
Maintaining, with no little heat,
Their various opinions.

That King, although no one denies,
His heart was of abnormal size,
Yet he'd have acted otherwise
If he had been acuter.
The end is easily foretold,
When every blessed thing you hold
Is made of silver, or of gold,
You long for simple pewter.
When you have nothing else to wear
But cloth of gold and satins rare,
For cloth of gold you cease to care—
Up goes the price of shoddy:
In short, whoever you may be,
To this conclusion you'll agree,
When every one is somebody,
Then no one's anybody!

SIR BARNABY BAMPTON BOO

This is Sir Barnaby Bampton Boo,
Last of a noble race,
Barnaby Bampton, coming to woo,
All at a deuce of a pace.
Barnaby Bampton Boo,
Here is a health to you:
Here is wishing you luck, you elderly buck—
Barnaby Bampton Boo!

The excellent women of Tuptonvee
Knew Sir Barnaby Boo;
One of them surely his bride would be,
But dickens a soul knew who.
Women of Tuptonvee,
Here is a health to ye:
For a Baronet, dears, you would cut off your ears,
Women of Tuptonvee!

Here are old Mr. and Mrs. de Plow
(Peter his Christian name),
They kept seven oxen, a pig, and a cow—
Farming it was their game.
Worthy old Peter de Plow,
Here is a health to thou:
Your race isn't run, though you're seventy-one,
Worthy old Peter de Plow!

To excellent Mr. and Mrs. de Plow
Came Sir Barnaby Boo,
He asked for their daughter, and told 'em as how
He'd fortune enough for two.
Barnaby Bampton's wealth,
Here is your jolly good health:
I'd never repine if you came to be mine,
Barnaby Bampton's wealth!

"O great SIR BARNABY BOO"
(Said PLOW to that titled swell),
"My missus has given me daughters two—
AMELIA and VOLATILE NELL!"
I hope you're uncommonly well:
You two pretty pearls—you extremely nice girls—
AMELIA and VOLATILE NELL!

"AMELIA is passable only, in face,
But, oh, she's a worthy girl;
Superior morals like hers would grace
The home of a belted Earl."
Morality, heavenly link!
To you I'll eternally drink:
I'm awfully fond of that heavenly bond,
Morality, heavenly link!

"Now NELLY's the prettier, p'raps, of my gals,
But, oh! she's a wayward chit;
She dresses herself in her showy fal-lals,
And doesn't read TUPPER a bit!"
O TUPPER, philosopher true,
How do you happen to do?
A publisher looks with respect on your books
For they *do* sell, philosopher true!

The Bart. (I'll be hanged if I drink him again,
Or care if he's ill or well),
He sneered at the goodness of MILLY THE PLAIN,
And cottoned to VOLATILE NELL!

O VOLATILE NELLY DE P.!
Be hanged if I'll empty to thee:
I like worthy maids, not mere frivolous jades,
VOLATILE NELLY DE P.!

They bolted, the Bart, and his frivolous dear,
And MILLY was left to pout;
For years they've got on very well, as I hear,
But soon he will rue it, no doubt.
O excellent MILLY DE PLOW,
I really can't drink to you now;
My head isn't strong, and the song has been long,
Excellent MILLY DE PLOW!

THE HOUSE OF PEERS

From *Iolanthe*

When Britain really ruled the waves—
(In good Queen Bess's time)
The House of Peers made no pretence
To intellectual eminence,
Or scholarship sublime;
Yet Britain won her proudest bays
In good Queen Bess's glorious days!

When Wellington thrashed Bonaparte,
As every child can tell,
The House of Peers, throughout the war,
Did nothing in particular,
And did it very well;
Yet Britain set the world ablaze
In good King George's glorious days!

And while the House of Peers withholds
  Its legislative hand,
And noble statesmen do not itch
To interfere with matters which
  They do not understand,
As bright will shine Great Britain's rays,
As in King George's glorious days!

A REGULAR ROYAL QUEEN

From *The Gondoliers*

Then one of us will be a Queen,
And sit on a golden throne,
With a crown instead,
Of a hat on her head,
And diamonds all her own!
With a beautiful robe of gold and green,
I've always understood;
I wonder whether
She'd wear a feather?
I rather think she should!

Oh, 'tis a glorious thing, I ween,
To be a regular Royal Queen!
No half-and-half affair, I mean,
But a right-down regular Royal Queen!
She'll drive about in a carriage and pair,
With the King on her left-hand side,
And a milk-white horse,
As a matter of course,
Whenever she wants to ride!
With beautiful silver shoes to wear
Upon her dainty feet;
With endless stocks
Of beautiful frocks
And as much as she wants to eat!

Whenever she condescends to walk,
Be sure that she'll shine at that,
With her haughty stare
And her nose in the air,
Like a well-born aristocrat!
At elegant high society talk
She'll bear away the bell,
With her "How de do?"
And her "How are you?"
And "I trust I see you well!"

And noble lords will scrape and bow,
And double themselves in two,
And open their eyes
In blank surprise
At whatever she likes to do.
And everybody will roundly vow
She's fair as flowers in May,
And say, "How clever!"
At whatsoever
She condescends to say!

Oh, 'tis a glorious thing, I ween,
To be a regular Royal Queen!
No half-and-half affair, I mean,
But a right-down regular Royal Queen!

THE HUMANE MIKADO

From *The Mikado*

A more humane Mikado never
Did in Japan exist;
To nobody second,
I'm certainly reckoned
A true philanthropist.
It is my very humane endeavour
To make, to some extent,
Each evil liver
A running river
Of harmless merriment.

My object all sublime
I shall achieve in time—
To let the punishment fit the crime—
The punishment fit the crime;
And make each prisoner pent
Unwillingly represent
A source of innocent merriment—
Of innocent merriment!

All prosy dull society sinners,
Who chatter and bleat and bore,
Are sent to hear sermons
From mystical Germans
Who preach from ten to four:
The amateur tenor, whose vocal villanies
All desire to shirk,
Shall, during off-hours,
Exhibit his powers
To Madame Tussaud's waxwork:
The lady who dyes a chemical yellow,
Or stains her grey hair puce,
Or pinches her figger,
Is painted with vigour
With permanent walnut juice:
The idiot who, in railway carriages,
Scribbles on window panes,
We only suffer
To ride on a buffer
In Parliamentary trains.

My object all sublime
I shall achieve in time—
To let the punishment fit the crime—
The punishment fit the crime;
And make each prisoner pent
Unwillingly represent
A source of innocent merriment—
Of innocent merriment!

The advertising quack who wearies
With tales of countless cures,
His teeth, I've enacted,
Shall all be extracted
By terrified amateurs:
The music-hall singer attends a series
Of masses and fugues and "ops"
By Bach, interwoven
With Spohr and Beethoven,
At classical Monday Pops:
The billiard sharp whom any one catches
His doom's extremely hard—
He's made to dwell
In a dungeon cell
On a spot that's always barred;
And there he plays extravagant matches
In fitless finger-stalls
On a cloth untrue
With a twisted cue,
And elliptical billiard balls!

My object all sublime
I shall achieve in time—
To let the punishment fit the crime—
The punishment fit the crime;
And make each prisoner pent
Unwillingly represent
A source of innocent merriment,
Of innocent merriment!

IV.

"LIST WHILE THE POET TROLLS"

Some Ridiculous Stories

ETIQUETTE

The *Ballyshannon* foundered off the coast of Cariboo,
And down in fathoms many went the captain and the crew;
Down went the owners—greedy men whom hope of gain
    allured:
Oh, dry the starting tear, for they were heavily insured.

Besides, the captain and the mate, the owners and the crew,
The passengers were also drowned excepting only two:
Young Peter Gray, who tasted teas for Baker, Croop,
    and Co.,
And Somers, who from Eastern shores imported indigo.

These passengers, by reason of their clinging to a mast,
Upon a desert island were eventually cast.
They hunted for their meals, as ALEXANDER SELKIRK used,
But they couldn't chat together—they had not been
introduced.

For PETER GRAY, and SOMERS too, though certainly in
trade,
Were properly particular about the friends they made;
And somehow thus they settled it without a word of
mouth—
That GRAY should take the northern half, while SOMERS
took the south.

On PETER's portion oysters grew—a delicacy rare,
But oysters were a delicacy PETER couldn't bear.
On SOMER's side was turtle, on the shingle lying thick,
Which SOMERS couldn't eat, because it always made him
sick.

GRAY gnashed his teeth with envy as he saw the mighty
store
Of turtle unmolested on his fellow-creature's shore:
The oysters at his feet aside impatiently he shoved,
For turtle and his mother were the only things he loved.

And SOMERS sighed in sorrow as he settled in the south,
For the thought of PETER's oysters brought the water to
his mouth.
He longed to lay him down upon the shelly bed, and stuff:
He had often eaten oysters, but had never had enough.

How they wished an introduction to each other they had
had
When on board the *Ballyshannon*! And it drove them
nearly mad
To think how very friendly with each other they might get,
If it wasn't for the arbitrary rule of etiquette!

One day, when out a-hunting for the *mus ridiculus*,
GRAY overheard his fellow-man soliloquising thus:
"I wonder how the playmates of my youth are getting on,
M'CONNELL, S. B. WALTERS, PADDY BYLES, and
ROBINSON?"

These simple words made PETER as delighted as could be,
Old chummies at the Charterhouse were ROBINSON and he!
He walked straight up to SOMERS, then he turned extremely
red,
Hesitated, hummed and hawed a bit, then cleared his
throat, and said:

"I beg your pardon—pray forgive me if I seem too bold,
But you have breathed a name I knew familiarly of old,
You spoke aloud of ROBINSON—I happened to be by—
You know him?" "Yes, extremely well." "Allow me—
so do I!"

It was enough: they felt they could more sociably get on,
For (ah, the magic of the fact!) they each knew ROBINSON!
And MR. SOMERS' turtle was at PETER's service quite,
And MR. SOMERS punished PETER's oyster-beds all night.

They soon became like brothers from community of
wrongs:
They wrote each other little odes and sang each other
songs;
They told each other anecdotes disparaging their wives;
On several occasions, too, they saved each other's lives.

They felt quite melancholy when they parted for the night,
And got up in the morning soon as ever it was light;
Each other's pleasant company they reckoned so upon,
And all because it happened that they both knew
ROBINSON!

They lived for many years on that inhospitable shore,
And day by day they learned to love each other more and
more.
At last, to their astonishment, on getting up one day,
They saw a vessel anchored in the offing of the bay!

To PETER an idea occurred, "Suppose we cross the main?
So good an opportunity may not occur again."
And SOMERS thought a minute, then ejaculated, "Done!
I wonder how my business in the City's getting on?"

"But stay," said MR. PETER: "when in England, as you
know,
I earned a living tasting teas for BAKER, CROOP, AND CO.,
I may be superseded—my employers think me dead!"
"Then come with me," said SOMERS, "and taste indigo
instead."

But all their plans were scattered in a moment when they
found
The vessel was a convict ship from Portland, outward
bound!
When a boat came off to fetch them, though they felt it
very kind,
To go on board they firmly but respectfully declined.

As both the happy settlers roared with laughter at the joke,
They recognized an unattractive fellow pulling stroke:
'Twas ROBINSON—a convict, in an unbecoming frock!
Condemned to seven years for misappropriating stock!!!

They laughed no more, for SOMERS thought he had been
rather rash
In knowing one whose friend has misappropriated cash;
And PETER thought a foolish tack he must have gone upon
In making the acquaintance of a friend of ROBINSON.

At first they didn't quarrel very openly, I've heard;
They nodded when they met, and now and then exchanged
a word:
The word grew rare, and rarer still the nodding of the head,
And when they meet each other now, they cut each other
dead.

To allocate the island they agreed by word of mouth,
And PETER takes the north again, and SOMERS takes the
south;
And PETER has the oysters, which he loathes with horror
grim,
And SOMERS has the turtle—turtle disagrees with him.

THE JUDGE'S SONG

From *Trial by Jury*

When I, good friends, was called to the Bar,
  I'd an appetite fresh and hearty,
But I was, as many young barristers are,
  An impecunious party.
I'd a swallow-tail coat of a beautiful blue—
  A brief which I bought of a booby—
A couple of shirts and a collar or two,
  And a ring that looked like a ruby!

In Westminster Hall I danced a dance,
  Like a semi-despondent fury;
For I thought I should never hit on a chance
  Of addressing a British Jury—
But I soon got tired of third-class journeys,

And dinners of bread and water;
So I fell in love with a rich attorney's
Elderly, ugly daughter.

The rich attorney, he wiped his eyes,
And replied to my fond professions:
"You shall reap the reward of your enterprise,
At the Bailey and Middlesex Sessions.
You'll soon get used to her looks," said he
"And a very nice girl you'll find her—
She may very well pass for forty-three
In the dusk, with a light behind her!"

The rich attorney was as good as his word:
The briefs came trooping gaily,
And every day my voice was heard
At the Sessions or Ancient Bailey.
All thieves who could my fees afford
Relied on my orations,
And many a burglar I've restored
To his friends and his relations.

At length I became as rich as the GURNEYS—
An incubus then I thought her,
So I threw over that rich attorney's
Elderly, ugly daughter.
The rich attorney my character high
Tried vainly to disparage—
And now, if you please, I'm ready to try
This Breach of Promise of Marriage!

THE TROUBADOUR

A troubadour he played
Without a castle wall,
Within, a hapless maid
Responded to his call.

"Oh, willow, woe is me!
Alack and well-a-day!
If I were only free
I'd hie me far away!"

Unknown her face and name,
But this he knew right well,
The maiden's wailing came
From out a dungeon cell.

A hapless woman lay
Within that prison grim—
That fact, I've heard him say,
Was quite enough for him.

"I will not sit or lie,
Or eat or drink, I vow,
Till thou art free as I,
Or I as pent as thou!"

Her tears then ceased to flow,
Her wails no longer rang,
And tuneful in her woe
The prisoned maiden sang:

"Oh, stranger, as you play
I recognise your touch;
And all that I can say,
Is thank you very much!"

He seized his clarion straight,
And blew thereat, until
A warder oped the gate,
"Oh, what might be your will?"

"I've come, sir knave, to see
The master of these halls:
A maid unwillingly
Lies prisoned in their walls."

With barely stifled sigh
  That porter dropped his head,
With teardrops in his eye,
  "A many, sir," he said.

He stayed to hear no more,
  But pushed that porter by,
And shortly stood before
  SIR HUGH DE PECKHAM RYE.

SIR HUGH he darkly frowned,
  "What would you, sir with me?"
The troubadour he downed
  Upon his bended knee.

"I've come, DE PECKHAM RYE,
  To do a Christian task,
You ask me what would I?
  It is not much I ask.

"Release these maidens, sir
  Whom you dominion o'er—
Particularly her
  Upon the second floor!

"And if you don't, my lord"—
  He here stood bolt upright,
And tapped a tailor's sword—
  "Come out at once and fight!"

SIR HUGH he called—and ran
  The warden from the gate,
"Go, show this gentleman
  The maid in forty-eight."

By many a cell they passed
  And stopped at length before
A portal bolted fast:
  The man unlocked the door.

He called inside the gate
  With coarse and brutal shout,
"Come, step it, forty-eight!"
  And forty-eight stepped out.

"They gets it pretty hot,
  The maidens wot we cotch—
Two years this lady's got
  For collaring a wotch."

"Oh, ah!—indeed—I see,"
The troubadour exclaimed—
"If I may make so free,
How is this castle named?"

The warden's eyelids fill,
And sighing, he replied,
"Of gloomy Pentonville
This is the Female Side!"

The minstrel did not wait
The warden stout to thank,
But recollected straight
He'd business at the Bank.

A DISCONTENTED SUGAR-BROKER

A gentleman of City fame
Now claims your kind attention;
West India broking was his game,
His name I shall not mention;
No one of finely pointed sense
Would violate a confidence,
And shall *I* go
And do it? No.
His name I shall not mention.

He had a trusty wife and true,
And very cosy quarters,
A manager, a boy or two,
Six clerks, and seven porters.
A broker must be doing well
(As any lunatic can tell)
Who can employ
An active boy,
Six clerks, and seven porters.

His knocker advertised no dun,
No losses made him sulky,
He had one sorrow—only one—
He was extremely bulky.
A man must be, I beg to state,
Exceptionally fortunate
Who owns his chief
And only grief
Is being very bulky.

"This load," he'd say, "I cannot bear,
I'm nineteen stone or twenty!
Henceforward I'll go in for air
And exercise in plenty."
Most people think that, should it come,
They can reduce a bulging tum
To measures fair
By taking air
And exercise in plenty.

In every weather, every day,
Dry, muddy, wet, or gritty,
He took to dancing all the way
From Brompton to the City.
You do not often get the chance
Of seeing sugar-brokers dance
From their abode
In Fulham Road
Through Brompton to the City.

He braved the gay and guileless laugh
Of children with their nusses,
The loud uneducated chaff
Of clerks on omnibuses.
Against all minor things that rack
A nicely balanced mind, I'll back
The noisy chaff
And ill-bred laugh
Of clerks on omnibuses.

His friends, who heard his money chink,
And saw the house he rented,
And knew his wife, could never think
What made him discontented.
It never entered their pure minds
That fads are of eccentric kinds,
Nor would they own
That fat alone
Could make one discontented.

"Your riches know no kind of pause,
Your trade is fast advancing,
You dance—but not for joy, because
You weep as you are dancing.
To dance implies that man is glad
To weep implies that man is sad.
But here are you
Who do the two—
You weep as you are dancing!"

His mania soon got noised about
And into all the papers—
His size increased beyond a doubt
For all his reckless capers:
It may seem singular to you
But all his friends admit it true—
The more he found
His figure round,
The more he cut his capers.

His bulk increased—no matter that—
He tried the more to toss it—
He never spoke of it as "fat"
But "adipose deposit."
Upon my word, it seems to me
Unpardonable vanity
(And worse than that)
To call your fat
An "adipose deposit."

At length his brawny knees gave way,
And on the carpet sinking,
Upon his shapeless back he lay
And kicked away like winking.
Instead of seeing in his state
The finger of unswerving Fate,
He laboured still
To work his will,
And kicked away like winking.

His friends, disgusted with him now,
Away in silence wended—
I hardly like to tell you how
This dreadful story ended.
The shocking sequel to impart,
I must employ the limner's art—
If you would know,
This sketch will show
How his exertions ended.

MORAL

I hate to preach—I hate to prate—
I'm no fanatic croaker,
But learn contentment from the fate
Of this West India broker.
He'd everything a man of taste
Could ever want, except a waist:
And discontent
His size anent,
And bootless perserverance blind,
Completely wrecked the peace of mind
Of this West India broker.

THE EXECUTIONER'S SONG

From *The Mikado*

The criminal cried, as he dropped him down,
  In a state of wild alarm—
With a frightful, frantic, fearful frown,
  I bared my big right arm.
I seized him by his little pig-tail,
  And on his knees fell he,
    As he squirmed and struggled,
    And gurgled and guggled,
  I drew my snickersnee!
      Oh, never shall I
      Forget the cry,
  Or the shriek that shriekéd he,
      As I gnashed my teeth,
      When from its sheath
  I drew my snickersnee!

He shivered and shook as he gave the sign
  For the stroke he didn't deserve;
When all of a sudden his eye met mine,
  And it seemed to brace his nerve;
For he nodded his head and kissed his hand,
  And whistled an air, did he,
      As the sabre true
      Cut cleanly through
  His cervical vertebrae!
Now though you'd have said that head was dead
  (For its owner dead was he),
It stood on its neck, with a smile well-bred,
  And bowed three times to me!
It was none of your impudent off-hand nods,
  But as humble as could be;
    For it clearly knew
    The deference due
  To a man of pedigree!
    And it's oh, I vow,
    This deathly bow
  Was a touching sight to see;
    Though trunkless, yet
    It couldn't forget
  The deference due to me!

THE GHOST'S HIGH NOON

From *Ruddigore*

When the night wind howls in the chimney cowls, and the
bat in the moonlight flies,
And inky clouds, like funeral shrouds, sail over the
midnight skies—
When the footpads quail at the night-bird's wail, and black
dogs bay the moon,
Then is the spectres' holiday—then is the ghosts' high
noon!

As the sob of the breeze sweeps over the trees, and the
mists lie low on the fen,
From grey tombstones are gathered the bones that once
were women and men,
And away they go, with a mop and a mow, to the revel
that ends too soon,
For cockcrow limits our holiday—the dead of the night's
high noon!

And then each ghost with his ladye-toast to their churchyard
beds take flight,
With a kiss, perhaps, on her lantern chaps, and a grisly
grim "good night";
Till the welcome knell of the midnight bell rings forth its
jolliest tune,
And ushers our next high holiday—the dead of the night's
high noon!

I AM THE CAPTAIN OF THE PINAFORE

From *H. M. S. Pinafore*

CAPTAIN: I am the Captain of the *Pinafore;*
CREW: And a right good Captain, too!
CAPT: You're very, very good,
And be it understood,
I command a right good crew.
Though related to a peer,
I can hand, reef, and steer,
And ship a selvagee;
I am never known to quail
At the fury of a gale,
And I'm never, never sick at sea!
CREW: What, never?
CAPT: No, never!
CREW: What, *never?*

CAPT: Hardly ever!
CREW: He's hardly ever sick at sea!
Then give three cheers and one cheer more,
For the hardy Captain of the *Pinafore!*

CAPT: I do my best to satisfy you all—
CREW: And with you we're quite content.
CAPT: You're exceedingly polite,
And I think it only right
To return the compliment.
Bad language or abuse,
I never, never use,
Whatever the emergency;
Though "Bother it" I may
Occasionally say,
I never use a big, big D—
CREW: What, never?
CAPT: No, never!
CREW: What, *never*?
CAPT: Hardly ever!
CREW: Hardly ever swears a big, big D—
Then give three cheers and one cheer more,
For the well-bred Captain of the *Pinafore*!

THE FIRST LORD'S SONG

From *H. M. S. Pinafore*

When I was a lad I served a term
As office boy to an Attorney's firm;
I cleaned the windows and I swept the floor,
And I polished up the handle of the big front door.
  I polished up that handle so carefullee,
  That now I am the Ruler of the Queen's Navee!

As office boy I made such a mark
That they gave me the post of a junior clerk;
I served the writs with a smile so bland,
And I copied all the letters in a big round hand.
  I copied all the letters in a hand so free,
  That now I am the Ruler of the Queen's Navee!

In serving writs I made such a name
That an articled clerk I soon became;
I wore clean collars and a brand-new suit
For the Pass Examination at the Institute:
 And that Pass Examination did so well for me,
 That now I am the Ruler of the Queen's Navee!

Of legal knowledge I acquired such a grip
That they took me into the partnership,
And that junior partnership I ween,
Was the only ship that I ever had seen:
 But that kind of ship so suited me,
 That now I am the Ruler of the Queen's Navee!

I grew so rich that I was sent
By a pocket borough into Parliament;
I alway's voted at my Party's call,
And I never thought of thinking for myself at all.
 I thought so little, they rewarded me,
 By making me the Ruler of the Queen's Navee!

Now, landsmen all, whoever you may be,
If you want to rise to the top of the tree—
If your soul isn't fettered to an office stool,
Be careful to be guided by this golden rule—
 Stick close to your desks and *never go to sea*,
 And you all may be Rulers of the Queen's Navee!

THE RIVAL CURATES

List while the poet trolls
  Of Mr. Clayton Hooper,
Who had a cure of souls
  At Spiffton-extra-Sooper.

He lived on curds and whey,
  And daily sang their praises,
And then he'd go and play
  With buttercups and daisies.

Wild croquet Hooper banned,
  And all the sports of Mammon,
He warred with cribbage, and
  He exorcised backgammon.

His helmet was a glance
  That spoke of holy gladness;
A saintly smile his lance,
  His shield a tear of sadness.

His Vicar smiled to see
   This armour on him buckled;
With pardonable glee
   He blessed himself and chuckled:

"In mildness to abound
   My curate's sole design is,
In all the country round
   There's none so mild as mine is!"

And HOOPER, disinclined
   His trumpet to be blowing,
Yet didn't think you'd find
   A milder curate going.

A friend arrived one day
   At Spiffton-extra-Sooper,
And in this shameful way
   He spoke to MR. HOOPER:

"You think your famous name
   For mildness can't be shaken,
That none can blot your fame—
   But, HOOPER, you're mistaken!

"Your mind is not as blank
   As that of HOPLEY PORTER,
Who holds a curate's rank
   At Assesmilk-cum-Worter.

"*He* plays the airy flute,
And looks depressed and blighted,
Doves round about him 'toot,'
And lambkins dance delighted.

"*He* labours more than you
At worsted work, and frames it;
In old maid's albums, too,
Sticks seaweed—yes, and names it!"

The tempter said his say,
Which pierced him like a needle—
He summoned straight away
His sexton and his beadle.

These men were men who could
Hold liberal opinions:
On Sundays they were good—
On week-days they were minions.

"To Hopley Porter go,
Your fare I will afford you—
Deal him a deadly blow,
And blessings shall reward you.

"But stay—I do not like
Undue assassination,
And so, before you strike,
Make this communication:

"I'll give him this one chance—
If he'll more gaily bear him,
Play croquet, smoke, and dance,
I willingly will spare him."

They went, those minions true,
To Assesmilk-cum-Worter,
And told their errand to
The Reverend Hopley Porter.

"What?" said that reverend gent,
  "Dance through my hours of leisure?
Smoke?—bathe myself with scent?—
  Play croquet? Oh, with a pleasure!

"Wear all my hair in curl?
  Stand at my door, and wink—so—
At every passing girl?
  My brothers, I should think so!

"For years I've longed for some
  Excuse for this revulsion:
Now that excuse has come—
  I do it on compulsion!!!"

He smoked and winked away—
  This REVEREND HOPLEY PORTER—
The deuce there was to pay
  At Assesmilk-cum-Worter.

And HOOPER holds his ground,
  In mildness daily growing—
They think him, all around,
  The mildest curate going.

V.

"NEVER, NEVER SICK AT SEA"

Admirals, Captains, and Jolly Jack Tars

THE YARN OF THE "NANCY BELL"

'Twas on the shores that round our coast
   From Deal to Ramsgate span,
That I found alone on a piece of stone
   An elderly naval man.

His hairy was weedy, his beard was long,
   And weedy and long was he,
And I heard this wight on the shore recite,
   In a singularly minor key:

"Oh, I am a cook and a captain bold,
   And the mate of the *Nancy* brig,
And a bo'sun tight, and a midshipmite,
   And the crew of the captain's gig."

And he shook his fists and he tore his hair,
Till I really felt afraid,
For I couldn't help thinking the man had been drinking,
And so I simply said:

"Oh, elderly man, it's little I know
Of the duties of men of the sea,
But I'll eat my hand if I understand
How you can possibly be

"At once a cook, and a captain bold,
And the mate of the *Nancy* brig,
And a bo'sun tight, and a midshipmite,
And the crew of the captain's gig."

Then he gave a hitch to his trousers, which
Is a trick all seamen larn,
And having got rid of a thumping quid,
He spun this painful yarn:

" 'Twas in the good ship *Nancy Bell*
That we sailed to the Indian sea,
And there on a reef we come to grief,
Which has often occurred to me.

"And pretty nigh all o' the crew was drowned
(There was seventy-seven o' soul),
And only ten of the *Nancy's* men
Said 'Here!' to the muster-roll.

"There was me and the cook and the captain bold,
And the mate of the *Nancy* brig,
And the bo'sun tight, and a midshipmite,
And the crew of the captain's gig.

"For a month we'd neither wittles nor drink,
Till a-hungry we did feel,
So we drawed a lot, and accordin' shot
The captain for our meal.

"The next lot fell to the *Nancy's* mate,
And a delicate dish he made;
Then our appetite with the midshipmite
We seven survivors stayed.

"And then we murdered the bo'sun tight,
And he much resembled pig;
Then we wittled free, did the cook and me,
On the crew of the captain's gig.

"Then only the cook and me was left,
And the delicate question, 'Which
Of us two goes to the kettle?' arose
And we argued it out as sich.

"For I loved that cook as a brother, I did,
And the cook he worshipped me;
But we'd both be blowed if we'd either be stowed
In the other chap's hold, you see.

"'I'll be eat if you dines off me,' says Tom,
  'Yes, that,' says I, 'you'll be,'—
'I'm boiled if I die, my friend,' quoth I,
  And 'Exactly so,' quoth he.

"Says he, 'Dear James, to murder me
  Were a foolish thing to do,
For don't you see that you can't cook *me*,
  While I can—and will—cook *you*!'

"So he boils the water, and takes the salt
  And the pepper in portions true
(Which he never forgot), and some chopped shallot,
  And some sage and parsley too.

" 'Come here,' says he, with a proper pride,
Which his smiling features tell,
" 'Twill soothing be if I let you see,
How extremely nice you'll smell.'

"And he stirred it round and round and round,
And he sniffed at the foaming froth;
When I ups with his heels, and smothers his squeals
In the scum of the boiling broth.

"And I eat that cook in a week or less,
And—as I eating be
The last of his chops, why, I almost drops,
For a wessel in sight I see!

* * * * *

"And I never grin, and I never smile,
And I never larf nor play,
But I sit and croak, and a single joke
I have—which is to say:

"Oh, I am a cook and a captain bold,
And the mate of the *Nancy* brig,
And a bo'sun tight, *and* a midshipmite,
And the crew of the captain's gig!"

THE BUMBOAT WOMAN'S STORY

I'm old, my dears, and shrivelled with age, and work, and grief,
My eyes are gone, and my teeth have been drawn by Time, the Thief!
For terrible sights I've seen, and dangers great I've run—
I'm nearly seventy now, and my work is almost done!

Ah! I've been young in my time, and I've played the deuce with men!
I'm speaking of ten years past—I was barely sixty then:
My cheeks were mellow and soft, and my eyes were large and sweet,
Poll Pineapple's eyes were the standing toast of the Royal Fleet!

A bumboat woman was I, and I faithfully served the ships
With apples and cakes, and fowls and beer, and halfpenny
dips,
And beef for the generous mess, where the officers dine at
nights,
And fine fresh peppermint drops for the rollicking
midshipmites.

Of all the kind commanders who anchored in Portsmouth
Bay,
By far the sweetest of all was kind LIEUTENANT BELAYE.
LIEUTENANT BELAYE commanded the gunboat *Hot Cross
Bun*,
She was seven and seventy feet in length, and she carried a
gun.

With the laudable view of enhancing his country's naval
pride,
When people inquired her size, LIEUTENANT BELAYE
replied,
"Oh, my ship, my ship is the first of the Hundred and
Twenty-ones!"
Which meant her tonnage, but people imagined it meant
her guns.

Whenever I went on board he would beckon me down
below,
"Come down, Little Buttercup, come" (for he loved to call
me so),

And he'd tell of the fights at sea in which he'd taken a part,
And so LIEUTENANT BELAYE won poor POLL PINEAPPLE'S heart!

But at length his orders came, and he said one day, said he,
"I'm ordered to sail with the *Hot Cross Bun* to the German Sea."
And the Portsmouth maidens wept when they learnt the evil day,
For every Portsmouth maid loved good LIEUTENANT BELAYE.

And I went to a back back street, with plenty of cheap cheap shops,
And I bought an oilskin hat, and a second-hand suit of slops,
And I went to LIEUTENANT BELAYE (and he never suspected *me*!)
And I entered myself as a chap as wanted to go to sea.

We sailed that afternoon at the mystic hour of one,—
Remarkably nice young men were the crew of the *Hot Cross Bun*.
I'm sorry to say that I've heard that sailors sometimes swear,
But I never yet heard a *Bun* say anything wrong, I declare.

When Jack Tars meet, they meet with a "Messmate, ho! What cheer?"
But here, on the *Hot Cross Bun*, it was "How do you do, my dear?"

When Jack Tars growl, I believe they growl with a big
big D—
But the strongest oath of the *Hot Cross Buns* was a mild
"Dear me!"

Yet though they were all well bred, you could scarcely call
them slick;
Whenever a sea was on, they were all extremely sick;
And whenever the weather was calm, and the wind was
light and fair,
They spent more time than a sailor should on his back back
hair.

They certainly shivered and shook when ordered aloft to
run,
And they screamed when LIEUTENANT BELAYE discharged
his only gun.
And as he was proud of his gun—such pride is hardly
wrong—
The Lieutenant was blazing away at intervals all day long.

They all agreed very well, though at times you heard it
said
That BILL had a way of his own of making his lips look
red—
That Joe looked quite his age—or somebody might declare
That BARNACLE's long pig-tail was never his own own hair.

BELAYE would admit that his men were of no great use to
him,
"But then," he would say, "there is little to do on a gunboat
trim.
I can hand, and reef, and steer, and fire my big gun too—
And it *is* such a treat to sail with a gentle well-bred crew."

I saw him every day! How the happy moments sped!
Reef topsails! Make all taut! There's dirty weather ahead!
(I do not mean that tempests threatened the *Hot Cross
Bun*:
In *that* case, I don't know whatever we *should* have done!)

After a fortnight's cruise we put into port one day,
And off on leave for a week went kind LIEUTENANT
BELAYE,
And after a long long week had passed (and it seemed like a
life),
LIEUTENANT BELAYE returned to his ship with a fair young
wife!

He up, and he says, says he, "Oh, crew of the *Hot Cross
Bun*,

Here is the wife of my heart, for the Church has made us
one!"
And as he uttered the word, the crew went out of their wits,
And all fell down in so many separate fainting fits.

And then their hair came down, or off, as the case might be,
And lo! the rest of the crew were simple girls, like me,
Who all had fled from their homes in a sailor's blue array,
To follow the shifting fate of kind LIEUTENANT BELAYE!

It's strange to think that *I* should ever have loved young
men,
But I'm speaking of ten years past—I was barely sixty then;
And now my cheeks are furrowed with grief and age, I
trow!
And poor POLL PINEAPPLE's eyes have lost their lustre
now!

VI.

"ROLL ON, THOU BALL, ROLL ON!"

The Way of the World

TO THE TERRESTRIAL GLOBE

BY A MISERABLE WRETCH

Roll on, thou ball, roll on!
Through pathless realms of Space
        Roll on!
What though I'm in a sorry case?
What though I cannot meet my bills?
What though I suffer toothache's ills?
What though I swallow countless pills?
      Never *you* mind!
        Roll on!

Roll on, thou ball, roll on!
Through seas of inky air
        Roll on!
It's true I have no shirts to wear;
It's true my butcher's bill is due;
It's true my prospects all look blue—
But don't let that unsettle you:
      Never *you* mind!
        Roll on!

It rolls on.

GIRL GRADUATES

From *Princess Ida*

They intend to send a wire
　　To the moon;
And they'll set the Thames on fire
　　Very soon;
Then they learn to make silk purses
　　With their rigs
From the ears of Lady Circe's
　　Piggy-wigs.
And weasels at their slumbers
　　They'll trepan;
To get sunbeams from cu*cum*bers
　　They've a plan.
They've a firmly rooted notion
They can cross the Polar Ocean,
And they'll find Perpetual Motion
　　If they can!

These are the phenomena
That every pretty domina
Hopes that we shall see
At this Universitee!

As for fashion, they forswear it,
So they say,
And the circle—they will square it
Some fine day;
Then the little pigs they're teaching
For to fly;
And from pulpits they'll be preaching
By-and-by!
Each newly-joined aspirant
To the clan
Must repudiate the tyrant
Known as Man;
They mock at him and flout him,
For they do not care about him,
And they're "going to do without him"
If they can!

These are the phenomena
That every pretty domina
Hopes that we shall see
At this Universitee!

THEY'LL NONE OF 'EM BE MISSED

From *The Mikado*

As some day it may happen that a victim must be found,
I've got a little list—I've got a little list
Of society offenders who might well be underground,
And who never would be missed—who never would be missed!
There's the pestilential nuisances who write for autographs—
All people who have flabby hands and irritating laughs—
All children who are up in dates, and floor you with 'em flat—
All persons who in shaking hands, shake hands with you like *that*—
And all third persons who on spoiling *tête-à-têtes* insist—
They'd none of 'em be missed—they'd none of 'em be missed!

There's the banjo serenader, and the others of his race,
And the piano organist—I've got him on the list!
And the people who eat peppermint and puff it in your face,
They never would be missed—they never would be missed!
Then the idiot who praises, with enthusiastic tone,
All centuries but this, and every country but his own;
And the lady from the provinces, who dresses like a guy,
And who "doesn't think she waltzes, but would rather like to try";
And that singular anomaly, the lady novelist—
I don't think she'd be missed—I'm *sure* she'd not be missed!

And that *Nisi Prius* nuisance, who just now is rather rife,
The Judicial humorist—I've got *him* on the list!
All funny fellows, comic men, and clowns of private life—
They'd none of 'em be missed—they'd none of 'em be missed!
And apologetic statesmen of the compromising kind,
Such as—What-d'ye-call-him—Thing'em-Bob, and likewise—Never mind,
And "St—'st—'st—and What's-his-name, and also—You know-who—
(The task of filling up the blanks I'd rather leave to *you*!)
But it really doesn't matter whom you put upon the list,
For they'd none of 'em be missed—they'd none of 'em be missed!

A NIGHTMARE

From *Iolanthe*

When you're lying awake with a dismal headache, and
    repose is taboo'd by anxiety,
I conceive you may use any language you choose to indulge
    in without impropriety;
For your brain is on fire—the bedclothes conspire of usual
    slumber to plunder you:
First your counterpane goes and uncovers your toes, and
    your sheet slips demurely from under you;
Then the blanketing tickles—you feel like mixed pickles,
    so terribly sharp is the pricking,
And you're hot, and you're cross, and you tumble and toss
    till there's nothing 'twixt you and the ticking.

Then the bedclothes all creep to the ground in a heap, and
you pick 'em all up in a tangle;
Next your pillow resigns and politely declines to remain at
its usual angle!
Well, you get some repose in the form of a doze, with hot
eyeballs and head ever aching,
But your slumbering teems with such horrible dreams that
you'd very much better be waking;
For you dream you are crossing the Channel, and tossing
about in a steamer from Harwich,
Which is something between a large bathing-machine and
a very small second-class carriage;
And you're giving a treat (penny ice and cold meat) to a
party of friends and relations—
They're a ravenous horde—and they all came on board at
Sloane Square and South Kensington Stations.
And bound on that journey you find your attorney (who
started that morning from Devon);
He's a bit undersized, and you don't feel surprised when
he tells you he's only eleven.
Well, you're driving like mad with this singular lad (by the
bye the ship's now a four-wheeler),
And you're playing round games, and he calls you bad
names when you tell him that "ties pay the dealer";
But this you can't stand, so you throw up your hand, and
you find you're as cold as an icicle,
In your shirt and your socks (the black silk with gold
clocks), crossing Salisbury Plain on a bicycle:
And he and the crew are on bicycles too—which they've
somehow or other invested in—

And he's telling the tars all the particu*lars* of a company
he's interested in—
It's a scheme of devices, to get at low prices, all goods
from cough mixtures to cables
(Which tickled the sailors) by treating retailers, as though
they were all vege*ta*bles—
You get a good spadesman to plant a small tradesman
(first take off his boots with a boot-tree),
And his legs will take root, and his fingers will shoot, and
they'll blossom and bud like a fruit-tree—
From the greengrocer tree you get grapes and green pea,
cauliflower, pineapple, and cranberries,
While the pastry-cook plant cherry-brandy will grant—
apple puffs, and three-corners, and banberries—
The shares are a penny, and ever so many are taken by
ROTHSCHILD and BARING,
And just as a few are allotted to you, you awake with a
shudder despairing—
You're a regular wreck, with a crick in your neck, and
no wonder you snore, for your head's on the floor, and
you've needles and pins from your soles to your
shins, and your flesh is a-creep, for your left leg's
asleep, and you've cramp in your toes, and a fly on
your nose, and some fluff in your lung, and a feverish
tongue, and a thirst that's intense, and a general sense
that you haven't been sleeping in clover;
But the darkness has passed, and it's daylight at last, and
the night has been long—ditto, ditto my song—and
thank goodness they're both of them over!

THE SUSCEPTIBLE CHANCELLOR

From *Iolanthe*

The law is the true embodiment
Of everything that's excellent.
It has no kind of fault or flaw,
And I, my lords, embody the Law.
The constitutional guardian I
Of pretty young Wards in Chancery,
All very agreeable girls—and none
Is over the age of twenty-one:
    A pleasant occupation for
    A rather susceptible Chancellor!

But though the compliment implied
Inflates me with legitimate pride,
It nevertheless can't be denied
That it has its inconvenient side.

For I'm not so old, and not so plain,
And I'm quite prepared to marry again,
But there'd be the deuce to pay in the Lords
If I fell in love with one of my Wards:
Which rather tries my temper, for
I'm *such* a susceptible Chancellor!

And every one who'd marry a Ward
Must come to me for my accord:
So in my court I sit all day,
Giving agreeable girls away,
With one for him—and one for he—
And one for you—and one for ye—
And one for thou— and one for thee—
But never, oh never a one for me
Which is exasperating, for
A highly susceptible Chancellor!

THE ENGLISHMAN

From *H. M. S. Pinafore*

He is an Englishman!
For he himself has said it,
And it's greatly to his credit,
That he is an Englishman!
For he might have been a Roosian,
A French, or Turk, or Proosian,
Or perhaps Itali-an!
But in spite of all temptations,
To belong to other nations,
He remains an Englishman!
Hurrah!
For the true-born Englishman!

VII.

"THE MEANING DOESN'T MATTER"

A Miscellany of Characters

THE AESTHETE

From *Patience*

Am I alone,
  And unobserved? I am!
Then let me own
  I'm an aesthetic sham!

This air severe
  Is but a mere
      Veneer!

This cynic smile
  Is but a wile
      Of guile!

This costume chaste
  Is but good taste
      Misplaced!

Let me confess!
A languid love for lilies does *not* blight me!
Lank limbs and haggard cheeks do *not* delight me!
I do *not* care for dirty greens
By any means.
I do *not* long for all one sees
That's Japanese
I am *not* fond of uttering platitudes
In stained glass attitudes,
In short, my mediaevalism's affectation,
Born of a morbid love of admiration!

If you're anxious for to shine in the high aesthetic line, as
a man of culture rare,
You must get up all the germs of the transcendental terms,
and plant them everywhere.
You must lie upon the daisies and discourse in novel
phrases of your complicated state of mind
The meaning doesn't matter if it's only idle chatter of a
transcendental kind.
And every one will say,
As you walk your mystic way,
"If this young man expresses himself in terms too deep
for *me*,
Why, what a very singularly deep young man this deep
young man must be!"

Be eloquent in praise of the very dull old days which have
long since passed away,
And convince 'em, if you can, that the reign of good

Queen Anne was Culture's palmiest day.
Of course you will pooh-pooh whatever's fresh and new, and declare it's crude and mean,
And that Art stopped short in the cultivated court of the Empress Josephine.
And every one will say,
As you walk your mystic way,
"If that's not good enough for him which is good enough for *me*,
Why, what a very cultivated kind of youth this kind of youth must be!"

Then a sentimental passion of a vegetable fashion must excite your languid spleen,
An attachment *à la* Plato for a bashful young potato, or a not-too-French French bean!
Though the Philistines may jostle, you will rank as an apostle in the high aesthetic band,
If you walk down Piccadilly with a poppy or a lily in your mediaeval hand.
And every one will say,
As you walk your flowery way,
"If he's content with a vegetable love which would certainly not suit *me*,
Why, what a most particularly pure young man this pure young man must be!"

THE DISCONCERTED TENOR

From *Utopia, Limited*

A tenor, all singers above
(This doesn't admit of a question),
Should keep himself quiet,
Attend to his diet,
And carefully nurse his digestion.
But when he is madly in love,
It's certain to tell on his singing—
You can't do chromatics
With proper emphatics
When anguish your bosom is wringing!
When distracted with worries in plenty,
And his pulse is a hundred and twenty,
And his fluttering bosom the slave of mistrust is,
A tenor can't do himself justice
Now observe—(*sings a high note*)—
You see, I can't do myself justice!

I could sing, if my fervour were mock,
It's easy enough if you're acting;
But when one's emotion
Is born of devotion,
You mustn't be over-exacting.
One ought to be firm as a rock
To venture a shake in *vibrato*;
When fervour's expected,
Keep cool and collected,
Or never attempt *agitato*.
But, of course, when his tongue is of leather,
And his lips appear pasted together,
And his sensitive palate as dry as a crust is,
A tenor can't do himself justice.
Now observe—(*sings a cadence*)—
It's no use—I can't do myself justice!

THE DISAGREEABLE MAN

From *Princess Ida*

If you give me your attention, I will tell you what I am:
I'm a genuine philanthropist—all other kinds are sham.
Each little fault of temper and each social defect
In my erring fellow-creatures, I endeavour to correct.
To all their little weaknesses I open people's eyes,
And little plans to snub the self-sufficient I devise;
I love my fellow-creatures—I do all the good I can—
Yet everybody says I'm such a disagreeable man!
And I can't think why!

To compliments inflated I've a withering reply,
And vanity I always do my best to mortify;
A charitable action I can skilfully dissect;
And interested motives I'm delighted to detect.
I know everybody's income and what everybody earns,
And I carefully compare it with the income-tax returns;
But to benefit humanity, however much I plan,
Yet everybody says I'm such a disagreeable man!
And I can't think why!

I'm sure I'm no ascetic: I'm as pleasant as can be;
You'll always find me ready with a crushing repartee;
I've an irritating chuckle, I've a celebrated sneer,
I've an entertaining snigger, I've a fascinating leer;
To everybody's prejudice I know a thing or two;
I can tell a woman's age in half a minute—and I do—
But although I try to make myself as pleasant as I can,
Yet everybody says I'm such a disagreeable man!
And I can't think why!

THE POLICEMAN'S LOT

From *The Pirates of Penzance*

When a felon's not engaged in his employment,
Or maturing his felonious little plans,
His capacity for innocent enjoyment
Is just as great as any honest man's.
Our feelings we with difficulty smother
When constabulary duty's to be done:
Ah, take one consideration with another,
A policeman's lot is not a happy one!

When the enterprising burglar's not a-burgling,
When the cut-throat isn't occupied in crime,
He loves to hear the little brook a-gurgling,
And listen to the merry village chime.
When the coster's finished jumping on his mother,
He loves to lie a-basking in the sun:
Ah, take one consideration with another,
The policeman's lot is not a happy one!

BUNTHORNE AND GROSVENOR'S DUET

From *Patience*

When I go out of door,
Of damozels a score
(All sighing and burning
And clinging and yearning)
Will follow me as before.
I shall, with cultured taste,
Distinguish gems from paste,
And "High diddle diddle"
Will rank as an idyll,
If I pronounce it chaste!

A most intense young man,
A soulful-eyed young man,
An ultra-poetical, super-aesthetical,
Out of the way young man!

Conceive me, if you can,
An every-day young man:
A commonplace type,
With a stick and a pipe
And a half-breed black-and-tan;
Who thinks suburban "hops"
More fun than "Monday Pops,"
Who's fond of his dinner,
And doesn't get thinner
On bottled beer and chops.

A commonplace young man,
A matter-of-fact young man,
A steady and stolid-y, jolly Bank-holiday
Every-day young man!

A Japanese young man,
A blue-and-white young man,
Francesca da Rimini, niminy, piminy,
Je-ne-sais-quoi young man!

A Chancery Lane young man,
A Somerset House young man,
A very delectable, highly respectable,
Threepenny bus young man!

A pallid and thin young man,
A haggard and lank young man,
A greenery-yallery, Grosvenor Gallery,
Foot in the grave young man!

A Sewell & Cross young man,
A Howell & James young man,
A pushing young particle—"What's the next article?"
Waterloo House young man!

LOST MR. BLAKE

MR. BLAKE was a regular out-and-out hardened sinner,
Who was quite out of the pale of Christianity, so to speak:
He was in the habit of smoking a long pipe and drinking a glass of grog on Sunday after dinner,
And seldom thought of going to church more than twice (or if Good Friday or Christmas Day happened to come in it) three times a week.

* * * *

This shocking old vagabond was so unutterably shameless
That he actually went a-courting a very respectable and pious middle-aged sister, by the name of BIGGS:
She was a rather attractive widow whose life, as such, had always been particularly blameless;
Her first husband had left her a secure but moderate competence owing to some fortunate speculations in the matter of figs.

She was an excellent person in every way—and won the
respect even of Mrs. Grundy,
She was a good housewife, too, and wouldn't have wasted
a penny if she had owned the Koh-i-noor;
She was just as strict as he was lax in her observance of
Sunday,
And being a good economist, and charitable besides, she
took all the bones and cold potatoes and broken
pie-crusts and candle-ends (when she had quite done
with them), and made them into an excellent soup for
the deserving poor.

I am sorry to say that she rather took to Blake—that
outcast of society;
And when respectable brothers who were fond of her
began to look dubious and to cough,
She would say, "Oh, my friends, it's because I hope to bring
this poor benighted soul back to virtue and propriety"
(And besides, the poor benighted soul, with all his
faults, was uncommonly well off).

And when Mr. Blake's dissipated friends called his
attention to the frown or the pout of her,
Whenever he did anything which appeared to her to
savour of an unmentionable place,
He would say she would be a very decent old girl when all
that nonsense was knocked out of her—
And his method of knocking it out of her is one that
covered him with disgrace.

She was fond of going to church services four times every
Sunday, and four or five times in the week, and never
seemed to pall of them,
So he hunted out all the churches within a convenient
distance that had services at different hours, so to
speak;
And when he had married her he positively insisted upon
their going to all of them,
So they contrived to do about twelve churches every
Sunday, and, if they had luck, from twenty-two to
twenty-three in the course of the week.

She was fond of dropping his sovereigns ostentatiously into
the plate, and she liked to see them stand out rather
conspicuously against the commonplace half-crowns
and shillings,
So he took her to all the charity sermons, and if by any
extraordinary chance there wasn't a charity sermon
anywhere, he would drop a couple of sovereigns (one
for him and one for her) into the poor-box at the door;
And as he always deducted the sums thus given in charity
from the housekeeping money, and the money he
allowed her for her bonnets and frillings,
She soon began to find that even charity, if you allow it
to interfere with your personal luxuries, becomes an
intolerable bore.
On Sundays she was always melancholy and anything but
good society,
For that day in her household was a day of sighings and

sobbings and wringing of hands and shaking of heads:
She wouldn't hear of a button being sewn on a glove, because it was a work neither of necessity nor of piety,
And strictly prohibited her servants from amusing themselves, or indeed doing anything at all except dusting the drawing-rooms, cleaning the boots and shoes, cooking the dinner, waiting generally on the family, and making the beds.

But BLAKE even went farther than that, and said that, on Sundays, people should do their own works of necessity, and not delegate them to persons in a menial situation,
So he wouldn't allow his servants to do so much as even answer a bell.

Here he is making his wife carry up the water for her bath to the second floor, much against her inclination,—
And why in the world the gentleman who illustrates these ballads has put him into a cocked hat is more than I can tell.

After about three months of this sort of thing, taking the smooth with the rough of it
(Blacking her own boots and peeling her own potatoes was not her notion of connubial bliss),
MRS. BLAKE began to find that she had pretty nearly had enough of it,
And came, in course of time, to think that BLAKE's own original line of conduct wasn't so much amiss.

And now that wicked person—that detestable sinner ("BELIAL BLAKE" his friends and well-wishers call him for his atrocities),
And his poor deluded victim whom all her Christian brothers dislike and pity so,
Go to the parish church only on Sunday morning and afternoon and occasionally on a week-day, and spend their evenings in connubial fondlings and affectionate reciprocities.
And I should like to know where in the world (or rather, out of it) they expect to go!

THE PLAYED-OUT HUMORIST

From *His Excellency*

Quixotic is his enterprise, and hopeless his adventure is,
Who seeks for jocularities that haven't yet been said.
The world has joked incessantly for over fifty centuries,
And every joke that's possible has long ago been made.
I started as a humorist with lots of mental fizziness,
But humour is a drug which it's the fashion to abuse;
For my stock-in-trade, my fixtures, and the goodwill of the business
No reasonable offer I am likely to refuse.
And if anybody choose
He may circulate the news
That no reasonable offer I'm likely to refuse.

Oh happy was that humorist—the first that made a pun
at all—
Who when a joke occurred to him, however poor and
mean,
Was absolutely certain that it never had been done at all—
How popular at dinners must that humorist have been!
Oh the days when some stepfather for the query held a
handle out,
The door-mat from the scraper, is it distant very far?
And when no one knew where Moses was when Aaron blew
the candle out,
And no one had discovered that a door could be a-jar!
But your modern hearers are
In their tastes particular,
And they sneer if you inform them that a door can be
a-jar!

In search of quip and quiddity, I've sat all day, alone,
apart—
And all that I could hit on as a problem was—to find
Analogy between a scrag of mutton and a Bony-part,
Which offers slight employment to the speculative mind:
For you cannot call it very good, however great your
charity—
It's not the sort of humour that is greeted with a shout—
And I've come to the conclusion that my mine of jocularity,
In present Anno Domini, is worked completely out!
Though the notion you may scout,
I can prove beyond a doubt
That my mine of jocularity is utterly worked out!

NOTES

"The Duke of Plaza-Toro"

paladin: a knight; hero.

"The Heavy Dragoon"

Paget: Sir James Paget (1814-1899), English brain surgeon.

Jullien: Louis Antoine Jullien (1812-1860), French composer.

Paddy: English slang for an Irishman.

Boucicault: Dion Boucicault, *Deé-on Boó-key-ko* (1820-1890), Irish-born dramatist and actor who wrote corny plays about the Irish, mostly performed in America.

Sodor and Man: a diocese which in Medieval times comprised the islands of the Hebrides and the Isle of Man.

D'Orsay: Alfred, Count D'Orsay (1801-1852), a French nobleman who cut a figure as a dandy and a rake in London society.

Victor Emmanuel: King Victor Emmanuel II of Italy (1820-1878), the first ruler to assume the title of "king" of Italy.

Peveril: the title character of Sir Walter Scott's novel *Peveril of the Peak.*

Doctor Sacheverell: Henry Sacheverell (1674-1724), English political preacher and clergyman.

Tupper: Martin Farquhar Tupper (1810-1889), English poetaster and popular philosopher whose best-known work was the moralizing *Proverbial Philosophy.*

Mr. Guizot: François Pierre Guillaume Guizot (1787-1874), French historian and statesman who was also a critic and biographer.

Lord Waterford: An Irish peer, famous as a huntsman.

Roderick Dhu: Scottish chieftain, appears in Sir Walter Scott's *The Lady of the Lake.*

Paddington Pollaky: an English detective, Ignatius Paul, who worked for Scotland Yard in the Paddington district of London.

Odalisque: a slave in a sultan's harem.

Sir Garnet: Garnet Joseph Wolseley, 1st Viscount Wolseley (1833-1913), British field marshal.

Manfred: king of Naples and Sicily (1232-1266).

Beadle of Burlington: a portly attendant at the Burlington Amusement Arcade.

Richardson's Show: an early traveling show, something like a circus.

Tussaud: Madame Tussaud, *Too-só* (1760-1850), founder of the famous London wax museum.

"ARAC'S SONG"

cuirass: armor covering the top of the body.

brassets: armor covering the arms.

"THE MODERN MAJOR-GENERAL"

Marathon: Greek plain where the Athenians, led by Miltiades, defeated the Persians in 490 B.C.

animalculous: of or related to animalcules, small animals nearly or entirely invisible to the human eye.

Sir Caradoc: Sir Cradock, a knight in King Arthur's court.

elegiacs: a verse form favored by the Greeks and Romans.

Heliogabalus: a high-living Roman emperor who ruled 218-222.

conics, parabolous: mathematical terms.

Gerard Dows: Gerrit Dou (1613-1675), Dutch painter, pupil of Rembrandt.

Zoffanies: John Zoffany (1733-1810), German-English painter noted for his portraits of actors.

Babylonic cuneiform: ancient form of writing, found in inscriptions dating back to 3800 B.C.

Caractacus: British king, circa A.D. 50.

mamelon: hillock; rounded elevation.

ravelin: part of a fort.

chassepot: a direct-action bolt gun, now obsolete.

commissariat: system by which armies are supplied with food.

sat a gee: sat on a horse.

"A MAN WHO WOULD WOO A FAIR MAID"

His twig he'll so carefully lime: a way of catching birds by smearing branches with a sticky substance.

"Ferdinando and Elvira"

Tupper: Martin Farquhar Tupper (1810-1889), English poetaster and popular philosopher, frequently mentioned jokingly by Gilbert.

popsy: term of endearment; sweetheart.

Coxwell and Glaisher: Henry Tracey Coxwell (1819-1900) and Dr. James Glaisher (1809-1903), English balloonists.

Henry Wadsworth: presumably Henry Wadsworth Longfellow (1807-1882), American poet.

Alfred: Alfred, Lord Tennyson (1809-1892), English poet laureate.

"Blue Blood"

Belgrave Square: a wealthy London neighborhood.

Seven Dials: lower-class district in London's East End.

"King Goodheart"

junket, jink: junket means to have a good time; "to go on a junket" is to go on a pleasure excursion; jink is merry-making, as in "high jinks."

shovel hat: kind of broad-brimmed hat worn by clergymen.

small beer: weak, inferior beer. In America we'd say "small potatoes."

shoddy: worthless stuff masquerading as something of quality.

"The Humane Mikado"

mystical Germans: at the time *The Mikado* was first produced, there was an influx of German Lutheran evangelists in London.

Parliamentary trains: in 1884 Parliament passed the Railway Act, some of whose regulations were regarded by the public as detrimental to railway service.
ops: operas.
Spohr: Louis Spohr (1784-1859), a German composer.
Monday Pops: "Popular Concerts" sponsored by the music publishers Chappell and Company.

"THE JUDGE'S SONG"

brief: a concise memorandum of the facts in a law case.
booby: an awkward, foolish person.
Westminster Hall: a court of justice in the city of Westminster, London.
Bailey: Old Bailey, London's main criminal court.
Middlesex: an English county.
Sessions: a period when courts are in session.
Gurneys: a rich family of the time.

"A DISCONTENTED SUGAR-BROKER"

nineteen stone or twenty: a stone is 14 pounds; thus, 266 or 280 pounds.

"I AM THE CAPTAIN OF THE PINAFORE"

ship a selvagee: to fasten a difficult nautical strap.

"THE YARN OF THE NANCY BELL"

wittled: dialect for victualed; ate.

"THE FIRST LORD'S SONG"

junior clerk: pronounced "clark," the English way.
writs: legal documents.
articled clerk: apprentice clerk.

the pass examination: examination to obtain a bachelor's degree at a British university.

pocket borough: a parliamentary constituancy controlled by one wealthy person or family.

"The Bumboat Woman's Story"

bumboat: small, wide boat which sells provisions to vessels lying offshore.

"Girl Graduates"

At the time Gilbert wrote this, it was considered a very odd thing indeed for women to attend college.

rigs: apparatuses for making things; looms.

Lady Circe's piggy-wigs: Greek sorceress who turned Ulysses' crew into swine.

domina: lady; woman of rank.

"They'll None of 'Em Be Missed"

the lady novelist: Martyn Green, the great Gilbert and Sullivan performer, writes, "At the time Gilbert wrote 'The Mikado,' she was regarded as a most singular anomaly, but as time went on and she became accepted, the point got lost, so Gilbert authorized the topicalization of the line. For many years the anomaly was the 'prohibitionist.' When that became obsolete another 'ist' was chosen. Among those used were the scorching motorist, jazz-time pianist, and—one I found to be more successful than all the others combined—the girl who's not been kissed!"

Nisi Prius: a legal term, here used to represent typical legal jargon.

dresses like a guy: like a grotesque person.

The Mikado was frequently performed before audiences of schoolchildren, so Gilbert wrote a special version of "They'll None of 'Em Be Missed" for such occasions:

As some day it may happen that a victim must be found,
I've made a little list—I've made a little list
Of inconvenient people who might well be underground,
For they never would be missed—they never would be missed.
The donkey who of nine-time six and eight-times seven prates
And stumps you with inquiries on geography and dates,
And asks for your ideas on spelling "parallelogram"—
All narrow-minded people who are stingy with their jam,
And the torture-dealing dentist, with the forceps in his fist—
They'd none of them be missed—they'd none of them be missed.
Then the teacher who for hours keeps you practicing your scales
With an ever-aching wrist—she never would be missed.
And children, too, who out of school are fond of telling tales.
They never would be missed—I'm sure they'd not be missed.
All people who maintain (in solemn earnest not in joke)
That quantities of sugar-plums are bad for little folk,
All those who hold the principle, unalterably fixed,
That instruction with amusement should most carefully be mixed:

All these (and many others) I have placed upon my list,
For they never would be missed—never, never would be missed.

"A Nightmare"

Harwich: English seaport, pronounced *hár-rich* to rhyme with *carriage*.

Sloane Square and South Kensington Stations: London subway stations.

Banburys: cakes first made in the town of Banbury, near Oxford.

Rothschild and Baring: English financial families.

"The Susceptible Chancellor"

Wards in Chancery: minors whose guardianship is vested in the Court of Chancery. It is contempt of court to marry a ward of chancery without the court's consent.

"The Englishman"

When it was suggested to Gilbert that this song should be rewritten for American audiences, he jokingly came up with this:

He is Ameri-can!
Though he himself has said it,
'Tis not much to his credit,
That he is Ameri-can!
For he might have been a Dutchman,
An Irish, Scotch, or such man,
Or perhaps an Englishman!
But in spite of hanky-panky,
He remains a true-born Yankee,
A cute Ameri-can!

"The Aesthete"

Oscar Wilde, the leading figure among the aesthetic young men of the 1880's, is satirized in this song.

"Bunthorne and Grosvenor's Duet"

suburban hops: dances held in the suburbs.

Monday Pops: concerts of popular music.

jolly Bank-holiday: a legal holiday in England, when the banks are closed, and very little business is done.

Francesca da Rimini: Italian lady of the thirteenth century who with her lover Paola was slain by her husband. Dante immortalized Paola and Francesca in the *Inferno*, placing them in the second circle.

miminy, piminy: affected, silly.

Chancery Lane: the section of London where the law firms are, thus, an area full of lawyer's clerks.

Somerset House: the office where all official records of births, deaths, etc., are kept.

threepenny bus young man: one who rides buses rather than taxis.

Grosvenor Gallery: a picture gallery in London.

Sewell & Cross, Howell & James, Waterloo House: London department stores.

"Lost Mr. Blake"

koh-i-noor: famous diamond, one of England's crown jewels.

Belial: the spirit of evil; the devil.

Mrs. Grundy: proper, strait-laced neighbor; "What will Mrs. Grundy say?"

"The Played-Out Humorist"

quiddity: a trifling point; a quibbling subtlety.

INDEX of TITLES

Aesthete, The 131
Arac's Song 22

Blue Blood 53
Bumboat Woman's Story, The 108
Bunthorne and Grosvenor's Duet 139

Contemplative Sentry, The 21

Disagreeable Man, The 136
Disconcerted Tenor, The 134
Discontented Sugar-Broker, A 84
Duke of Plaza-Toro, The 13

Englishman, The 127
Etiquette 71
Executioner's Song, The 89

Ferdinando and Elvira, or, the Gentle Pieman . . . 40
First Lord's Song, The 94

General John 15
Gentle Alice Brown 33
Ghost's High Noon, The 91
Girl Graduates 118

Heavy Dragoon, The 19
House of Peers, The 61
Humane Mikado, The 65

I Am the Captain of the *Pinafore* 92

Judge's Song, The 77

King Goodheart 55

Lost Mr. Blake 141

Magnet and the Churn, The 38
Man Who Would Woo a Fair Maid, A 29
Modern Major-General, The 24
Modest Couple, The 46

Nightmare, A 122

Played-Out Humorist, The 146
Policeman's Lot, The 138

Regular Royal Queen, A 63
Rival Curates, The 96

Sir Barnaby Bampton Boo 57

Suicide's Grave, The 31
Susceptible Chancellor, The 125

They'll None of 'Em Be Missed 120
To Phoebe 45
To the Terrestrial Globe 117
Troubadour, The 79

Yarn of the "Nancy Bell," The 103

INDEX of FIRST LINES

A gentleman of City fame 84
A magnet hung in a hardware shop 38
A man who would woo a fair maid 29
A more humane Mikado never 65
A tenor, all singers above 134
A troubadour he played 79
Am I alone 131
As some day it may happen that a victim must be
found 120
At a pleasant evening party I had taken down to
supper 40

"Gentle, modest, little flower," 45

He is an Englishman 127

I am the Captain of the *Pinafore* 92
I am the very pattern of a modern Major-Gineral . 24
If you give me your attention, I will tell you what
I am 136
If you want a receipt for that popular mystery 19
I'm old, my dears, and shrivelled with age, and
work, and grief 108
In enterprise of martial kind 13
It was a robber's daughter, and her name was ALICE
BROWN 33

List while the poet trolls 96

MR. BLAKE was a regular out-and-out hardened
sinner 141

On a tree by a river a little tomtit 31

Quixotic is his enterprise, and hopeless his
adventure is 146

Roll on, thou ball, roll on 117

Spurn not the nobly born 53

The *Ballyshannon* foundered off the coast of
Cariboo 71
The bravest names for fire and flames 15
The criminal cried, as he dropped him down 89
The law is the true embodiment 125
Then one of us will be a Queen 63

There lived a King, as I've been told 55
They intend to send a wire 118
This helmet, I suppose 22
This is SIR BARNABY BAMPTON BOO 57
'Twas on the shores that round our coast 103

When a felon's not engaged in his employment . . . 138
When all night long a chap remains 21
When Britain really ruled the waves 61
When I go out of door 139
When I, good friends, was called to the Bar 77
When I was a lad I served a term 94
When man and maiden meet, I like to see a
drooping eye 46
When the night wind howls in the chimney cowls,
and the bat in the moonlight flies 91
When you're lying awake with a dismal headache,
and repose is taboo'd by anxiety 122